STATE OF ILLINOIS
ADLAI E. STEVENSON, *Governor*
DEPARTMENT OF REGISTRATION AND EDUCATION
C. HOBART ENGLE, *Director*

DIVISION OF THE
STATE GEOLOGICAL SURVEY
M. M. LEIGHTON, *Chief*
URBANA

BULLETIN NO. 77

GEOLOGY AND MINERAL RESOURCES

OF THE

CARLINVILLE QUADRANGLE

BY

JOHN R. BALL

PRINTED BY AUTHORITY OF THE STATE OF ILLINOIS

URBANA, ILLINOIS

1952

ORGANIZATION

STATE OF ILLINOIS
HON. ADLAI E. STEVENSON, *Governor*
DEPARTMENT OF REGISTRATION AND EDUCATION
HON. C. HOBART ENGLE, *Director*

BOARD OF NATURAL RESOURCES AND CONSERVATION

GEOLOGICAL SURVEY DIVISION
M. M. LEIGHTON, PH.D., *Chief*

GENERAL ADMINISTRATION
(Not including part-time personnel)

LIBRARY
ANNE E. KOVANDA, B.S., B.L.S., *Librarian*
RUBY D. FRISON, *Technical Assistant*

MINERAL RESOURCE RECORDS
VIVIAN GORDON, *Head*
DOROTHY GORE, B.S., *Research Assistant*
BEVERLY SOLLIDAY, B.S., *Research Assistant*
SARAH HARALDSEN, *Technical Assistant*
CAROLYN HARPER, A.B., *Technical Assistant*
C. MARCIA WOOD, B.A., *Technical Assistant*
BARBARA H. ORKILD, *Technical Assistant*
GRETCHEN B. BAUERLE, *Technical Assistant*
MARGERY FRIES, B.S., *Technical Assistant*

PUBLICATIONS
JANE V. OLSON, B.A., *Associate Technical Editor*
BARBARA A. ZEIDERS, B.S., *Assistant Editor*
MEREDITH M. CALKINS, *Geologic Draftsman*
LIDIA SELKREGG, D.N.S., *Assistant Geologic Draftsman*

TECHNICAL RECORDS
BERENICE REED, *Supervisory Technical Assistant*
MARILYN DELAND, B.S., *Technical Assistant*

GENERAL SCIENTIFIC INFORMATION
IRENE H. BENSON, *Technical Assistant*
GWENDOLYN DAVIS, *Technical Assistant*

March 1, 1952

OTHER TECHNICAL SERVICES
LESLIE D. VAUGHAN, *Research Associate*
BEULAH M. UNFER, *Technical Assistant*
A. W. GOTSTEIN, *Research Associate*
GLENN G. POOR, *Research Associate*
GILBERT L. TINBERG, *Technical Assistant*
WAYNE W. NOFFTZ, *Supervisory Technical Assistant*
ROBERT M. FAIRFIELD, *Technical Assistant*

FINANCIAL RECORDS
VELDA A. MILLARD, In Charge
LEONA B. KENWARD, *Clerk-Typist III*
VIRGINIA C. SANDERSON, B.S., *Clerk-Typist II*
MAXINE BRAMEL, *Clerk-Typist I*
EMILY MARIE H. BROWNFIELD, B.S., *Clerk-Typist I*
JOANN M. DUNBAR, *Clerk-Typist I*

CLERICAL SERVICES
MARY CECIL, *Clerk-Stenographer III*
MARY M. SULLIVAN, *Clerk-Stenographer III*
ETHEL M. HENWOOD, *Clerk-Stenographer II*
LYLA NOFFTZ, *Clerk-Stenographer II*
HAZEL V. ORR, *Clerk-Stenographer I*
SHIRLEY W. RICE, *Clerk-Stenographer I*
BARBARA J. BOAS, *Clerk-Stenographer I*
MARY J. DE HAAN, *Messenger-Clerk I*

AUTOMOTIVE SERVICE
GLENN G. POOR, In Charge
ROBERT O. ELLIS, *Automotive Mechanic*
EVERETTE EDWARDS, *Automotive Mechanic*

FOREWORD

Although the field work on which this report is based was done principally in 1929 and 1930, the author, either alone or in company with other members of the Illinois Geological Survey, briefly visited the area occasionally while assembling other data and preparing the report, until he completed the final draft about January 1, 1945. Consequently the data in the report are essentially as of that date. However, the nomenclature, classification, and correlation of the geological formations have been brought up to date as of July 1, 1951.

M. M. LEIGHTON, *Chief*

CONTENTS

ILLUSTRATIONS

TABLES

PLATES
(*In pocket*)

GEOLOGY AND MINERAL RESOURCES OF THE CARLINVILLE QUADRANGLE

BY

JOHN R. BALL

CHAPTER I — INTRODUCTION

LOCATION AND AREA

THE CARLINVILLE quadrangle is located in the southwestern part of Illinois, about 25 miles south of Springfield (fig. 1). It is entirely within Macoupin County and is bounded on the east and west, respectively, by the meridians of 89°45′ and 90° W., and on the north and south by parallels 39°30′ and 39°15′ N. It is 13.4 miles wide and 17 miles long, and its area is 231.82 square miles. The city of Carlinville, from which the quadrangle is named, is located near the middle of the south end of the quadrangle.

MINERAL RESOURCES

Coal, formerly mined extensively in the quadrangle, is one of the significant mineral resources of the area. Some oil and gas has been produced. Limestone for crushed stone and for agricultural fertilizer has been quarried at numerous places. Clays and shales suitable for common brick and tile, and some gravel for road materials, are present. The soils are of great importance and the groundwater resources are indispensable.

ACKNOWLEDGMENTS

Numerous present and former members of the Illinois State Geological Survey staff have given valuable assistance in the field studies and in the preparation of this report. C. E. Needham and Denard Lee served as field assistants in 1929 and 1930, respectively. Perry McClure, E. T. Benson, and W. B. Roe determined the elevations of critical outcrops, test borings, and mine shafts.

FIG. 1.—Index map showing the location of the Carlinville quadrangle.

G. H. Cady, Head of the Coal Division at that time, directed the field work in 1929 and subsequently advised concerning coal resources and Pennsylvanian stratigraphy. Since 1930 the work has been under the direction of George E. Ekblaw, Head of the Division of Engineering Geology and Topographic Mapping and in charge of areal geology until 1945, who visited the field several times, assisted in some of the Pleistocene mapping, and generally supervised the preparation of the report.

M. M. Leighton, Chief of the Illinois Geological Survey, and Paul MacClintock, while a member of the Survey staff, reviewed the Pleistocene deposits, suggested interpretations of them, and assisted in their mapping. J. Marvin Weller, former Head of the Stratigraphy and Paleontology Division, and Harold R. Wanless, Research Affiliate in Geology, visited most of the outcrops of Pennsylvanian strata and advised concerning their correlation. Paul Herbert, Jr., a former member of the Survey, studied the available samples and correlated the pre-Pennsylvanian formations in available records of wells in and adjacent to the quadrangle.

J. E. Lamar, Head of the Industrial Minerals Division, prepared the portions of the economic geology chapter relating to shale and clay, sand and gravel, building stone, and limestone, and Robert R. Storm, a former staff member, prepared the portion relating to groundwater aquifers. Frank C. Baker, then Curator, Natural History Museum, University of Illinois, identified the Pleistocene fossils, and A. C. Noé, formerly Paleobotanist, identified the Pennsylvanian plant fossils. G. H. Cady, J. M. Weller, A. H. Bell, Head of the Oil and Gas Division, and Ralph E. Grim, former Head of the Clay Resources and Clay Mineral Technology Division, J. E. Lamar, and L. E. Workman, former Head of the Subsurface Division, have critically read those portions of the manuscript relating to their particular fields. Numerous citizens in Carlinville and its vicinity gave many helpful services, and their friendly interest in the work is greatly appreciated.

FUNDAMENTAL GEOLOGIC PROCESSES

There are familiar natural agencies which are actively modifying the earth's surface. The falling of rains, the slow movement of water in the ground, and the movement of streams toward the sea are activities wherein water is the chief agent. The movements of winds and of glaciers, the growth of vegetation, the work of animals, including man, the chemical decay of rocks, and their mechanical disintegration are other geological processes. Other less obvious phenomena include diastrophism, or slow elevation or depression of parts of the earth's crust; former diastrophic movements are revealed by the present attitude or slope of the bedrock formations. Ancient deposition of sea-bottom sediments is recorded in the indurated rocks.

THE WORK OF RUNNING WATER

The attacks by running water upon the surface of the land are accomplished (1) by the runoff on slopes during and after heavy rainfall and (2) by streams. Gullies, first relatively short and small (fig. 2), are worn in the land by the repeated concentration of running water over one course for short lengths of time. Some relatively large gullies may contain running water intermittently; only stream valleys that are cut deep enough to intersect the permanent groundwater table have a continuous flow.

When a large stream maintains its flow through a valley that it is at the same time creating, its erosion may be more or less obvious. In an area of relatively slight relief, as in the Carlinville quadrangle, the valleys do not become very deep but may be many miles in length and fairly wide. The limit of downward cutting of any stream is determined by the surface of the body of water into which it flows, and when this limit is reached, the stream will begin to plane laterally. The stream will undermine its banks against which it swings, and thus will widen its valley.

THE WORK OF GROUNDWATER

Rain water that passes immediately into the ground becomes groundwater. The water standing in wells is groundwater. Groundwater has a slow movement downward and laterally, hence it is in circulation and is constantly seeking its lowest possible level, in this respect repeating the movements of the surface waters. Only under certain unusual conditions, however, is

FIG. 2.—Gully developed by running water, NW ¼ sec. 34, T. 11 N., R. 8 W. (South Palmyra Twp.). Erosion has been encouraged by forest-clearing and cultivation. Topography of the valley before the development of the gully is revealed by the contour of the original slopes.

there any movement of groundwater that resembles stream flow. Groundwater is capable of dissolving and carrying away earth minerals, thus tending to lower the surface of the land. It may perform other mechanical and chemical changes which are very important geologically, although outwardly not conspicuous. They are particularly important in the development and the renewal of soils.

The Work of Winds

The capacity of winds to sustain and to transport dust and sands is recognized readily in arid regions where vegetation is lacking or scarce. The natural and cultivated growths of vegetation in the Carlinville quadrangle are sufficient to check effective wind work almost completely, although an appreciable amount of dust may be blown from plowed land, either during dry seasons or when exposed during an open winter. During glacial times, however, the winds transported dust from silt-laden valley trains and deposited it over the land surface to form loess.

The Work of Glaciers

Existing glaciers are notably restricted to definite regions of the globe. In former stages of earth history, during glacial epochs, however, areas now remote from existing glaciers were invaded by vast sheets of slowly spreading ice. The continental glaciers once invaded the northern Mississippi Valley region practically to the south end of Illinois, as shown in several ways. Its erosive work on the bedrock is revealed by several occurrences of striae (scratches) near Carlinville and elsewhere. The aggregate of clays, sand, gravel, and scattered larger boulders, obtained from bedrock formations lying to the north, is known collectively as "drift" (figs. 4, 16-19). Unstratified clay, frequently studded with cobblestones and larger boulders, is till, or boulder clay, often called "hardpan." Drift is deposited so abundantly over the Carlinville quadrangle that the preglacial landscape is concealed. Vestiges of soils, drainage ways, and interglacial deposits, developed between successive glacial advances, are found (geologic sections 38-47, 50-52). Buried logs, traces of peat, and fossil shells of land molluscs have been seen in the ravine east of Blackburn College. In the crushed rock material is mineral matter available for plant food and thus, together with the clay and gravel, the former glaciers have provided materials of significant economic value.

Other Geological Processes

Processes less subject to observation than the ones outlined above are also active. When the water in the ground freezes, its increase in volume breaks up the rocks and forces stones and boulders from the frost-zone to the surface.

The bedrock in the Carlinville quadrangle is all sedimentary, that is, derived by consolidation of sediments, some of which contain fossils of marine organisms, indicating former submergences of the area beneath sea waters.

The coal beds, however, represent another type of inundation. Coal is derived from vegetable matter preserved from complete decay by a covering of water. Thus, it is related to peat, which is formed under the waters of ponds and swamps, where vegetation fallen in the water is preserved from season to season. Such accumulations after burial, under great pressure, and after ages of time finally become coal.

CHAPTER II — PHYSIOGRAPHY

RELIEF AND DRAINAGE

The landscape features of the Carlinville quadrangle, which lies in the Springfield Plain of the Till Plains section of the Central Lowland province,[1] are those common to a well-dissected till plain.

Disregarding valleys, the upland area of the quadrangle is a featureless plain, sloping gently from the north towards the south and southeast. The highest land, in the northwest, is between 690 and 700 feet above sea level. Slightly west of Carlinville the average elevation is about 620 to 630 feet. The total relief, that is, the maximum vertical difference in elevations in the quadrangle, ranges from 150 to 170 feet. The extremes lie in opposite ends of the quadrangle so that the relief is not impressive.

From evidence supplied by test borings it is known that the total relief of the bedrock surface (pl. 1) is greater than that of the present surface. The differences of rock surface elevations, however, do not parallel surface elevations. It is evident that the gentle inclination and the slight relief of the present surface are related more to continental glaciation than to the bedrock surface.

TOPOGRAPHY OF THE UPLANDS

JACKSONVILLE MORAINE

The elevations of many of the low hills in the vicinity of Virden and Girard are about the same as that of the highest land in the quadrangle, north of Modesto. Hills of this elevation do not extend over the entire quadrangle but are more abundant in the northern and northeastern parts (pl. 1). They are visible from State Highway 4, south of Girard, and are numerous between Virden and Girard. They extend west of Virden into the east-central part of North Otter Township. The hills and the slightly higher land they surmount form the drainage divide not only between Sugar Creek (T. 12 N., R. 7 W.) and Otter and Macoupin creeks but also between Sangamon and Macoupin rivers.

They constitute the Jacksonville moraine, a marginal moraine developed at the edge of the Illinoian glacier during a time when the ice was melting rapidly. The moraine extends to the east through the north half of the Waverly quadrangle to the vicinity of Jacksonville, Ill., where it is prominently developed.

The inconspicuous hills or mounds of the moraine are lower, more elongate, and more gently sloping than those customarily found in marginal moraines. Formerly, the irregularities of the moraine probably were more pronounced, but they have been masked by a great amount of loess and have been reduced by erosion.

COOPS MOUND

The more or less elliptical ridge called Coops Mound (fig. 3) is the most conspicuous elevation in the Carlinville quadrangle. In the E $\frac{1}{2}$ sec. 17 and SW $\frac{1}{4}$ sec. 9, T. 10 N., R. 6 W. (Shaw Point Twp.), it is named after an early settler in Macoupin County.[2] It consists of two hills, the higher of which rises to the same elevation as the high land of the quadrangle, north of Modesto, or from 60 to 80 feet above the uplands to the west. The valley flat of Macoupin Creek east of it is from 100 to 120 feet lower than its summit. Its northern and western slopes are cultivated, but the eastern slopes are covered with brush and timber.

UPLAND PRAIRIE

The remaining area of the quadrangle is divided between uplands and valley slopes and flats. The uplands are nearly as they were at the close of Pleistocene time, although they have been aggraded slightly by the extensive deposits of loess which cover

[1]Leighton, M. M., Ekblaw, George E., and Horberg, Leland, Physiographic divisions of Illinois: Illinois Geol. Survey Rept. Inv. 129, table 1, figs. 1 and 2, pp. 26-28, 1948.

[2]Walker, Charles A., History of Macoupin County: Brink, McDonough, and Co., 1879.

FIG. 3.—Eastward view of Coops Mound in the E ½ sec. 17, T. 10 N., R. 6 W. (Shaw Point Twp.).

them. Certain broad, linear swales in the uplands may represent part of drift-filled preglacial valleys, but in the main the uplands represent the undissected portion of the till plain and constitute broad stream divides or interfluves. The upland flat is almost level, except for the gentle southward slope previously mentioned. The descent from uplands to stream valleys is generally a brush-covered slope too steep for cultivation. Where a stream flows directly against its valley wall, it cuts steep banks (fig. 4).

The greatest expanse of slightly dissected upland is in the south-central part of the quadrangle, north and northwest of Carlinville and South Standard.

Minor features of the uplands possibly have been eliminated or modified by man. In the SE ¼ sec. 17, T. 12 N., R. 7 W. (North Otter Twp.) is a slight depression about 350 to 400 feet long northeast-southwest and about 150 feet long northwest-southeast. It is choked with a growth of willows, sedge, swamp sourdock, and smartweed and contains an abundance of crayfish burrows. Poorly drained depressions are a feature of glacial topography, but de-

pressions as slight as this one possibly could be drained and cultivated. If this has been the practice, depressions of this type in the quadrangle formerly may have been more abundant. Some of the broadened valley heads may represent depressions of this type drained by the headward extension of the present drainage lines.

SLUMPING OF THE UPLANDS

Some of the upland slopes and valley walls are modified by "slump," a phenomenon produced by the combined effects of groundwater and gravity. When soil and subsoil on sufficiently steep slopes become thoroughly saturated with water, the material either will slip down the slope in a slow, flowing motion or will give way in a series of displaced steps, converting the slope into extremely rough broken ground.

In the Carlinville area slumping has been facilitated in some instances by the presence of a shale ("soapstone") underlying till. When the surface of the shale becomes wet, it tends to serve as a lubricant and thus contributes to easier movement down the

Fig. 4.—Stream-cut bank in the SE ¼ sec. 10, T. 11 N., R. 7 W. (South Otter Twp.) about two miles northwest of Nilwood, exposing Illinoian till on Yarmouth peat (see fig. 17).

valley slopes. An excellent example of this phenomenon occurs in the broad valley east of Mr. Leopold's farmhouse in the W½ sec. 2, T. 9 N., R. 7 W. (Brushy Mound Twp.) (fig. 5).

DEVELOPMENT OF DRAINAGE SYSTEM

There are two large streams in the quadrangle, Macoupin and Otter creeks. The headwaters of Macoupin Creek are in the Raymond quadrangle, east of the Carlinville. The headwaters of Otter Creek are within the boundaries of the quadrangle. Massa Creek, a large tributary of Otter Creek, and Hurricane Creek, a large tributary of Macoupin Creek, also have their headwaters within the quadrangle. All these streams, together with Bear Creek, Lick Creek, and others, tend to maintain nearly parallel courses from northeast to southwest across the quadrangle. Most of the larger and longer tributaries enter the master streams from the north and west, but in the southeastern part of the quadrangle Shaw Point Branch and Sugar Creek enter Macoupin Creek from the south and east. In the north half of the quadrangle there is a leaf-like or dendritic type of drainage pattern. It seems evident that most streams flow in harmony with the general slope away from the moraine in the northern and northeastern parts of the quadrangle. In the extreme southeast of the quadrangle area, however, the streams are flowing against the regional slope.

TYPES OF VALLEYS

For the greater part of their courses across the quadrangle, the larger streams have wide flat-bottomed valleys, suitable for cultivation. The valleys of both Macoupin and Otter creeks attain widths of a half mile in places. Where these valleys are deepest, their flats lie some 70 to 90 feet below the average upland levels. The flats of many of the smaller streams are also wide enough for cultivation or for pasture purposes. Hurricane Creek valley, west of Carlinville, is an example.

In most instances, the valley walls descend from upland to valley flat without any step-like intermediate benches or terraces. However, along the 2½ miles of Macoupin Creek below the abandoned Womac branch of the Alton Railway, there are terraces 10 to 30 feet above the valley flat. A few poorly preserved terraces, possibly belonging

FIG. 5.—Slumping of valley slopes three miles southeast of Carlinville, induced by shales underlying the glacial drift in the SW ¼ sec. 2, T. 9 N., R. 7 W. (Brushy Mound Twp.).

to the same level, occur upstream from the old railroad grade.

Terraces of the type described above are called alluvial terraces because they consist of material deposited by the streams during earlier stages of valley development. The terraces in the lower valley of Macoupin Creek contain some gravel overlain extensively with loess.

Rock terraces are similar in appearance to alluvial terraces but consist of bedrock, bare or covered only thinly with soil. They occur particularly where sedimentary rocks in nearly horizontal beds are encountered by the downward cutting of the streams so that in time the more resistant beds tend to stand out in benches along the course of the valley. There are a few rock terraces in the quadrangle. One is in the east valley wall of Macoupin Creek, immediately south of the abandoned Alton Railway bridge, east of Carlinville. Here the Shoal Creek limestone forms a grass-covered bench about 15 feet above the valley flat. The Carlinville limestone forms small rock terraces in small valleys in the southern part of Carlinville. In a large gully northeast of Mr. May's farmhouse in the NE ¼ sec. 3, T. 9 N., R. 7 W. (Brushy Mound

Twp.), the Macoupin limestone forms relatively broad rock terraces.

CONSTRUCTIONAL VALLEYS

Another type of valley in the Carlinville quadrangle is one that has not been developed by the stream that now occupies it. Most often the upper course of a stream valley, it is a poorly defined linear depression, its floor sometimes but a few feet below the level of the uplands and at a higher altitude than the floor of the normal valley. It is frequently trenched by a stream which has cut a narrow gorge through it, generally no wider than the stream. It either may be a depression over a preglacial valley or may have been produced where a remnant of the glacier became isolated and covered entirely with drift so that when it finally melted, it created a subsidence of the surface. Inasmuch as valleys of this type are not in any respect the work of stream erosion but are connected with the depositional work of the glaciers, they are referred to as "constructional valleys."

Sugar Creek, partly within Shaw Point Township, east of Carlinville, has a valley that in part is possibly constructional, especially in the upper extension which reaches into Honey Point Township. From its junction with the valley of Macoupin Creek, south of Coops Mound, upstream to the abandoned fill of the Alton Railway, the valley appears to be stream cut, but south of the railroad the valley changes in character: a few contours, widely separated, indicate a gentle valley-wall slope and a slight depression. The stream is intermittent, and fairly deep pools along its course indicate that it has done but little vertical cutting. In this broad and shallow valley, marshy conditions exist along the stream. These features are typical of constructional valleys, yet the pools and marshy floor of the valley may be due to shale that is here buried only slightly below the surface of the land (pl. 1). The course of Sugar Creek is more or less parallel to the course of Macoupin Creek, yet the water flows in the opposite direction; this valley is an exception to the general relationships of the tributary system of valleys.

CHAPTER III — PRE-PENNSYLVANIAN STRATIGRAPHY

Bedrock is concealed throughout most of the Carlinville quadrangle by glacial drift, but there are a limited number of outcrops and numerous wells by means of which it is possible to gain a fair picture of the composition and character and of the structural relations of the buried strata.

The bedrock exposed in the quadrangle belongs to the McLeansboro group of the Pennsylvanian system (table 1). Many wells penetrate the McLeansboro group as deeply as the Herrin (No. 6) coal bed, and a few go somewhat deeper. Ten wells (table 2) within the quadrangle penetrate the entire Pennsylvanian system and enter older Paleozoic formations. The Plattin formation in the upper part of the Ordovician system is the oldest penetrated by any of these wells; information concerning the lower Ordovician formations, all of the Cambrian system, and the pre-Cambrian rocks must be obtained from records of wells outside the quadrangle.

PRE-CAMBRIAN SYSTEMS

Granite or other crystalline rock of pre-Cambrian age presumably lies below all the sedimentary rocks. It has been reached in wells in St. Louis, Missouri,[1] 50 miles southwest of Carlinville, and in Ralls County, Missouri,[2] about 90 miles nearly due west of Carlinville, at depths of 3,844 feet and 2,200 feet, respectively. In Pike County, Ill., 70 miles northwest from Carlinville, another deep well reaches quartzite at a depth of 3,205 feet.[3]

On the basis of these data and the known thicknesses of pre-Galena formations in these wells and others in south-central Illinois, it is estimated that the pre-Cambrian rocks underlie the Carlinville quadrangle at a depth of approximately 5,000 feet.

CAMBRIAN SYSTEM[4]

The Cambrian system consists of a number of sandstone, sandy dolomite, and dolomite formations that have an estimated total thickness of about 2,000 feet in the vicinity of Carlinville. In Missouri these formations, from bottom to top, are named La Motte, Bonneterre, Davis, Derby-Doe Run, Potosi, Eminence, and Proctor. In Wisconsin the formations of Cambrian age, from bottom to top, are named Mt. Simon, Eau Claire, Galesville, Franconia, Trempealeau, and Jordan, and these names have been used for the Cambrian formations encountered in wells in Illinois as far south as the central part of the state. There are some uncertainties in the correlation of the formations represented by the two sets of names, and it is not certain which would be more appropriate in the Carlinville area.

ORDOVICIAN SYSTEM[5]

The Ordovician rocks of Illinois are divided into four series as follows: Prairie du Chien, Chazyan, Mohawkian, and Cincinnatian. However, only the four youngest formations of the Ordovician system, namely the Plattin, Decorah, and Galena (Kimmswick) formations of the Mohawkian series and the Maquoketa formation of the Cincinnatian series, have been encountered in wells in the Carlinville quadrangle (see record of Fuller and Turner-Chamness No. 1 well, Appendix B, No. 1, and plate 2). Below the Plattin formation in succession are the Joachim, Dutchtown, Glenwood (?), St. Peter, Shakopee, New Richmond, and Oneota formations.

[1]Fenneman, N. M., The geology and mineral resources of the St. Louis quadrangle, Missouri-Illinois: U. S. Geol. Survey Bull. 438, p. 16, 1911.

[2]McQueen, H. S., et al., The Lincoln fold in Lincoln, Pike, and Ralls counties, northeastern Missouri: Guidebook of Fifteenth Annual Field Conference, Kansas Geol. Soc., p. 101, 1941.

[3]Herndon-Campbell No. 1 well, NW ½ sec. 15, T. 4 S., R. 5 W. (Hadley Twp.).

[4]The name is derived from Cambria, the Roman name for northern Wales, where the rocks of this system are typically exposed. Sedgwick. Rev. A., Edinburgh New Philos. Jour., vol. 19, p. 390, Aug. 14, 1835 (abst.).

[5]The name is derived from the tribe of Ordovices which during the Roman occupation lived in Wales, where these rocks are typically exposed. Lapworth, C., On the tripartite classification of the lower Paleozoic rocks: Geol. Mag., London, new series, vol. 6, pp. 12-14, 1879.

TABLE 1.—GEOLOGIC COLUMN

Era	System	Series	Group	Formation	Material
CENOZOIC	Pleistocene			Recent	Alluvium, slope wash, wind deposits Till, boulders, gravel, silt, clay
	Tertiary				Gravel
PALEOZOIC	Pennsylvanian		McLeansboro Carbondale Tradewater Caseyville		Sandstone, shale, clay, limestone, coal
	Mississippian	Chester			Shale and sandstone
		Iowa	Meramec	Ste. Genevieve St. Louis Salem	Limestone, silty, sandy, and oolitic Limestone, some dolomite Limestone and dolomite
			Osage	Warsaw Keokuk Burlington Fern Glen	Shale, siltstone, and sandstone Limestone, cherty Limestone, shaly and silty
			Kinderhook	Chouteau Hannibal Louisiana Grassy Creek	Limestone, slightly silty, dolomitic and glauconitic Shale and siltstone, some oolitic limestone Limestone, dense, buff Shale, dark brown to black
	Devonian			Cedar Valley Wapsipinicon	Limestone or dolomite, cherty, with red sandstone at base Limestone and dolomite with some sandstone
	Silurian	Niagaran			Dolomite, cherty Limestone
		Alexandrian		Sexton Creek Edgewood	Dolomite, cherty Dolomite, sandy, cherty, slightly silty, argillaceous
	Ordovician	Cincinnatian		Maquoketa	Shale and some siltstone, calcareous, micaceous, and carbonaceous
		Mohawkian		Galena (Kimmswick) Decorah Plattin Joachim	Limestone, occasionally dolomitic Limestone or dolomite, argillaceous Limestone, some interbedded dolomite
		Chazyan		Dutchtown Glenwood St. Peter	
		Prairie du Chien		Shakopee New Richmond Oneota	
	Cambrian				

Pre-Cambrian

TABLE 2.—WELLS PENETRATING PRE-PENNSYLVANIAN STRATA
IN THE CARLINVILLE QUADRANGLE

Name of Well	Location	Depth in feet	Lowest formation penetrated
Hayes-Alderson..................	NE ¼ sec. 17, T. 12 N., R. 7 W. (North Otter Twp.)	616	St. Louis
Lagers-Bristow 1.................	NE ¼ sec. 7, T. 11 N., R. 7 W. (South Otter Twp.)	1487	Niagaran
Northwestern Macoupin Coal Co. Contract 1....................	NE ¼ sec. 4, T. 11 N., R. 8 W. (South Palmyra Twp.)	875	Keokuk
*Phillips-Giller 1.................	NW ¼ sec. 15, T. 11 N., R. 8 W. (South Palmyra Twp.)	1828	Plattin
Standard Oil Co.................	NE ¼ sec. 9, T. 10 N., R. 6 W. (Shaw Point Twp.)	695	Ste. Genevieve
Schell-Hauer 1..................	NW ¼ sec. 25, T. 10 N., R. 7 W. (Carlinville Twp.)	792	Warsaw-Salem
*Fuller and Turner-Chamness 1.....	NE ¼ sec. 4, T. 9 N., R. 6 W. (Honey Point Twp.)	2253	Galena (Kimmswick)
Mid-Continent-Bernhardt.........	NE ¼ sec. 5, T. 9 N., R. 6 W. (Honey Point Twp.)	1593	Wapsipinicon
Bridge-Feiker 1..................	SW ¼ sec. 1, T. 9. N., R. 7 W. (Brushy Mound Twp.)	1622	Wapsipinicon
Chrysler-Hall 1..................	SW ¼ sec. 5, T. 9 N., R. 7 W. (Brushy Mound Twp.)	2100	Plattin

*Records of these wells are published in Appendix B. Records of other wells are available for reference and for loan at the Illinois State Geological Survey.

PLATTIN FORMATION[6]

Only two wells in the Carlinville quadrangle are deep enough to encounter the Plattin formation (table 2 and pl. 2). It is a relatively pure limestone with some layers of interbedded dolomite. It ranges from light gray to buff to light brown, and usually varies from medium to finely crystalline, but it is occasionally sublithographic. The total thickness of the Plattin limestone in the Carlinville quadrangle is probably about 400 feet,[7] but the maximum thickness penetrated by the Chrysler-Hall No. 1 well is 85 feet. The Plattin formation is overlain conformably by the Decorah formation.[8]

The upper part of the Plattin formation, which has been penetrated by the wells in the Carlinville quadrangle, is the southern equivalent of the Platteville formation of the Upper Mississippi Valley region.[9]

DECORAH FORMATION[10]

As identified in wells in and near the Carlinville quadrangle, the Decorah formation consists of buff to brown, fine-grained to medium-grained, crystalline to dense dolomite and limestone, with a little greenish-gray shale. It ranges from 6 to 20 feet in thickness. It is conformable with or gradational into the underlying Plattin formation, but it is separated from the overlying Galena (Kimmswick) formation by an unconformity.[11]

It is possible that these strata are correlative with the Spechts Ferry member of the Plattin (Platteville) formation as it is recognized in northwestern Illinois.[12]

[6]The name Plattin was proposed "for the fine grained limestone formation between the Kimmswick and 'First Magnesian' (Joachim by later usage) and which has generally been called either Trenton or lower Trenton . . . The formation takes its name from Plattin Creek, Jefferson County (Missouri), near the mouth of which it is well exposed."
The formation was named by Ulrich in 1904 *in* Buckley, E. R., and Buehler, H. A., Quarrying industry of Missouri: Missouri Bur. Geol. and Mines, vol. 2, 2nd series, p. 111, 1904.

[7]Du Bois, E. P., Subsurface relations of the Maquoketa and "Trenton" formations in Illinois: Illinois Geol. Survey Rept. Inv. 105, pl. 1, wells 6 and 7; pl. 2, wells 3 and 4, 1945.

[8]Du Bois, E. P., *op. cit.*, pp. 23 and 24.

[9]Du Bois, E. P., *op. cit.*, p. 25 and pl. 1.

[10]The Decorah formation was named from exposures at the village of Decorah, Winneshiek County, Iowa. Calvin, Samuel, Geology of Winneshiek County: Iowa Geol. Survey, vol. 16, pp. 60-61, 84-85, 1907.

[11]Du Bois, *op. cit.*, p. 23.

[12]Du Bois, *op. cit.*, p. 21.

GALENA[13] (KIMMSWICK[14]) FORMATION

The Galena (Kimmswick) formation is a light buff to light gray finely to coarsely crystalline limestone or slightly dolomitic limestone, with occasional silty facies and with some brownish or reddish organic inclusions. It ranges from 100 to 120 feet in thickness, the maximum in the area being reported in a well in the southeast of the quadrangle. It is unconformable with both the underlying Decorah and the overlying Maquoketa formations.[15]

Formerly the name Kimmswick was applied to these strata in southern Illinois, but as recent studies have shown that they are continuous with the lower part of the Galena dolomite of the Upper Mississippi Valley, the older name takes precedence, and the local name is used only parenthetically to prevent confusion.[16]

CINCINNATIAN SERIES[17]

MAQUOKETA FORMATION[18]

The Maquoketa formation consists dominantly of shale but includes much limestone, dolomite, siltstone, and sandstone.[19] A limestone bed 25 feet thick was reported in the Phillips-Giller No. 1 well in the western part of the Carlinville quadrangle. This limestone bed probably represents the middle limestone member of the Maquoketa formation.[19] Some of the shale is calcareous, there are some mica and carbonaceous materials, and siltstone is freely interbedded with the shale. Most of the formation is light gray to greenish gray, but some is brown to brownish gray. Some of the shale is friable, some is tough and resistant.

Where fossils occur, the texture commonly is coarser than otherwise.

The Maquoketa formation is the thickest of the Ordovician formations penetrated by deep wells in the Carlinville quadrangle. Its thickness ranges from 170 to 202 feet, which is slightly greater than at points farther west and less than in eastern Illinois.[20]

The Maquoketa formation is separated from both the underlying and overlying formations by extensive unconformities.[21]

SILURIAN SYSTEM[22]

The Silurian system in Illinois is composed of the Alexandrian and the Niagaran series. In the study of samples from wells in the Carlinville quadrangle no attempt was made to differentiate the formations of the Niagaran series, and in some cases the formations of the Alexandrian series also were not separated.

ALEXANDRIAN SERIES[23]

The typical locality for the Alexandrian series is in the southwestern part of Illinois, where it is divided into the Orchard Creek, Girardeau, Edgewood, and Sexton Creek formations. Of these, only the Edgewood and the Sexton Creek formations are recognized in the samples from wells in the Carlinville quadrangle.

EDGEWOOD FORMATION[24]

The Edgewood limestone has been recognized positively in the Phillips-Giller No. 1 well and doubtfully in the Fuller and Turner-Chamness No. 1 well in the Carlinville quadrangle. In the other well that penetrated Silurian strata the Alexandrian is undifferentiated.

[13]So named because this formation is the principal lead-bearing zone in the Upper Mississippi Valley. It is well developed in the vicinity of Galena (Illinois). Dubuque (Iowa), and Mineral Point (Wisconsin).
Foster, J. W., and Whitney, J. D., Report on the geology of the Lake Superior land district: pt. 2, pp. 146-148, 1851.
[14]This name was proposed to apply "to the more or less crystalline limestone being quarried at Graysboro, Cape Girardeau, Glen Park, Kimmswick, and other localities in southeastern Missouri" by Ulrich *in* Buckley and Buehler, *op. cit.*, p. 111.
[15]Du Bois, E. P., *op. cit.*, pp. 14-15, 19, 22-23.
[16]Du Bois, E. P., *op. cit.*, p. 17.
[17]The Cincinnatian series derives its name from exposures in Ohio and Kentucky in the vicinity of Cincinnati. Meek, F. B. and Worthen, A. H., Acad. Nat. Sci. Philadelphia Proc., vol. 17, p. 155, 1865.
[18]Named for Little Maquoketa River in Dubuque County, Iowa. White, C. A., Geol. Survey of Iowa, vol. 1, p. 181, 1870.
[19]Du Bois, E. P., *op. cit.*, pp. 7-13, figs. 2 and 3.

[20]Du Bois, E. P., *op. cit.*, fig. 1, pp. 8, 14.
[21]Du Bois, E. P., *op. cit.*, pp. 14-15.
[22]The name Silurian was derived from Silures, an ancient Celtic people living in the southwestern part of the British Isles at the time of the Roman conquest. Murchison, R. I., On the Silurian system of rocks: London and Edinburgh Philos. Mag. and Jour. Sci., 3rd series, vol. 7, pp. 46-62, July 1835.
[23]The name Alexandrian is derived from Alexander County, Ill. Savage, T. E., On the Lower Paleozoic stratigraphy of southwestern Illinois: Am. Jour. Sci., 4th series, vol. 25, pp. 433-434, 1908.
[24]The name Edgewood is derived from the village of Edgewood, Pike County, Mo. Savage, T. E., Ordovician and Silurian formations in Alexander County, Illinois: Am. Jour. Sci., 4th ser., vol. 28, p. 517, 1909.

The Edgewood is commonly a light brown or light grayish-brown, dense to finely crystalline sandy dolomite. In some places it is cherty, in two instances it is slightly vesicular in texture, and in a few instances it is slightly silty and argillaceous. A three-foot oolitic limestone at the base of the Edgewood formation in the Phillips-Giller No. 1 well suggests that Noix oolite of the Cyrene member[25] of the Edgewood may be present.

In the Carlinville quadrangle the Edgewood limestone is at least 20 feet thick in the Phillips-Giller No. 1 well and is 30 feet thick in the Fuller and Turner-Chamness No. 1 well. Elsewhere in the vicinity of the quadrangle its thickness ranges between 8 and 24 feet.

The Edgewood formation is unconformable on the underlying beds over a wide area in the Lower Mississippi Valley, but possibly this unconformity does not occur everywhere in the Upper Mississippi Valley.[26] It is unconformable, also, under the Sexton Creek formation.

In the Upper Mississippi Valley, the Edgewood formation is recognized by its fossils although in Iowa and Wisconsin different formation names are used. It has been correlated with the Manitoulin dolomite of northern Michigan and with a part of the Chimneyhill formation in Oklahoma.[27]

SEXTON CREEK FORMATION[28]

The Sexton Creek limestone is a white, light gray, or light grayish-buff, generally cherty dolomite or dolomitic limestone. It usually is speckled with green or is stained green by the glauconite which it contains. The presence of glauconite is a distinctive feature of this rock and of its correlatives in many places.

In the two Carlinville quadrangle wells where the Sexton Creek is distinguished its thickness is 20 and 22 feet. In nearby localities its thickness is slightly greater.

The unconformity below the Sexton Creek formation has been mentioned and above it there is a disconformity.[29]

When identifying and naming the members of the Alexandrian series, Savage[30] recognized the correlation of the Sexton Creek limestone with the Brassfield limestone of Kentucky, Tennessee, and Ohio. This correlation is well established on a faunal basis, the brachiopod species, *Triplesia ortoni,* identifying the Brassfield (Sexton Creek) over wide areas. Savage[31] also correlated the Kankakee formation of northern Illinois with the Brassfield formation.

NIAGARAN SERIES[32]

In the Carlinville quadrangle the surface of the Niagaran series lies at depths ranging from 1275 feet in the Phillips-Giller No. 1 well to 1630 feet in the Fuller and Turner-Chamness No. 1 well, or at elevations 700 to 992 feet below sea level. The surface of the series thus slopes from the northwest to the southeast at a rate of about 22 feet per mile.

The Niagaran series in the Carlinville quadrangle is seemingly a transition between the rocks of the series exposed respectively in southern Illinois and in northern Illinois, as it exhibits lithologic features which occur in both areas. The upper part of the series has a high proportion of cherty dolomite and in this respect is like the Niagaran of the Upper Mississippi Valley. The lower part is a purer limestone, ranging between light gray and white, but conspicuously mottled with small pale brown areas that have centers of pale pink calcite, strikingly

[25]Savage, T. E., Stratigraphy and paleontology of the Alexandrian series in Illinois and Missouri: Illinois Geol. Survey Bull. 23, pp. 76, 77, 1917.
[26]Ball, J. R., Stratigraphy of the Silurian system of the Lower Mississippi Valley: Guidebook of the Thirteenth Annual Field Conference, Kansas Geol. Soc., p. 116, 1939.
[27]Ball, J. R., op. cit., p. 117, footnotes.
[28]The Sexton Creek limestone was so named because it occurs in the bluff overlooking Sexton Creek where that stream follows the foot of the Mississippi River bluff. Savage, T. E., The Ordovician and Silurian formations in Alexander County, Illinois: Am. Jour. Sci., 4th ser., vol. 28, p. 518, 1909.

[29]Willman, H. B., and Payne, J. N., Geology and mineral resources of the Marseilles, Ottawa, and Streator quadrangles: Illinois Geol. Survey Bull. 66, p. 69, 1942.
[30]Savage, T. E., On the lower Paleozoic stratigraphy of southwestern Illinois: Amer. Jour Sci., 4th series, vol. 25, p. 43, 1908.
[31]Savage, T. E., Correlation of the Silurian formations of North America: Geol. Soc. Amer. Bull., vol. 53, chart 3, 1942. In this chart the name of Sexton Creek does not appear.
[32]This series derives its name from Niagara Falls where it is well developed. Hall, James, Report of the survey of the fourth geological district: Natural History of New York, part 4, Geology of New York, vol. 4, p. 80, 1843.

similar to the rock in outcrops in the Lower Mississippi Valley. Its texture is generally finely crystalline, but is locally dense and sublithographic. The Niagaran series ranges from 175 to 265 feet thick in the quadrangle, definitely thickening towards the southeast.

The unconformity below the Niagaran series has been noted. The absence of Upper Silurian and Lower Devonian formations which occur elsewhere in the state[33] indicates an extensive unconformity also at the top of the Niagaran series.

The lower part of the Niagaran series in the quadrangle, which is characterized by rock with pinkish mottling, is probably correlative with the Osgood-Laurel members of the Bainbridge formation of southern Illinois and Missouri[34] and the Joliet and Waukesha formations of northern Illinois. The upper, more dolomitic facies of the Niagaran series is correlative with the upper part of the Niagaran series in the Upper Mississippi Valley.

DEVONIAN SYSTEM[35]

The Devonian system is represented in the Carlinville quadrangle by two formations, the Wapsipinicon and Cedar Valley limestones, both of Middle Devonian age.

WAPSIPINICON FORMATION[36]

In the northwest part of the Carlinville quadrangle the Wapsipinicon formation consists of light buff to light brownish-gray, fine-grained to very fine-grained sublithographic sandy limestone. In the southeast part of the quadrangle it consists of sandy limestone and sandy dolomite, with sand beds both at the top and at the bottom. The limestone is white, light gray, light buff, or light brown, usually very fine-grained to lithographic but sometimes fine- to medium-grained. The dolomite is usually brownish,

very fine-grained to dense, generally crystalline and partly vesicular, and locally cherty.

Thicknesses of 10 feet and 24 feet are reported in the northwest part of the quadrangle, whereas in the southeast part they are 66 feet and 116 feet; thus is revealed a great thickening from northwest to southeast across the quadrangle. Beneath the Wapsipinicon limestone is a great erosional unconformity. The variability in thickness of the formation beneath the overlying Cedar Valley formation at many localities is evidence of an unconformity between them.

The Wapsipinicon formation is probably the correlative of the lower part of the Grand Tower limestone, and the sandstone that occurs at the base of the formation in the south part of the quadrangle may be correlative with the Dutch Creek sandstone of Middle Devonian age in Union County, Ill.[37] The sandstone that occurs at the top of the formation in the south part of the quadrangle may be the equivalent of the Hoing sand, the oil-bearing stratum in the Colmar-Plymouth pool in western Illinois.

CEDAR VALLEY FORMATION[38]

The Cedar Valley formation has been identified only in the wells in the northwest part of the quadrangle and is absent in those in the southeast part, unless the sandstone bed included in the top of the Wapsipinicon formation is actually Cedar Valley in age.

It consists of light brown or light brownish-gray, fine to very finely crystalline dolomite, and light gray to buff very finely crystalline to dense very sandy cherty limestone. Locally, it includes gray, very fine- to medium-grained sandstone, in part dolomitic and silty. Its thickness is reported as 16 and 28 feet in the quadrangle, but it ranges up to as much as 70 feet in the region around it.

Unconformities occur both beneath and above the formation. The Cedar Valley formation may be correlated either with the upper part of the Grand Tower formation

[33]Workman, L. E., Subsurface geology of the Devonian system in Illinois: Illinois Geol. Survey Bull. 68, p. 195, 1944.

[34]Ball, J. R., Some Silurian correlations in Lower Mississippi drainage basin: Bull. Am. Assoc. Petrol. Geol., vol. 26, p. 18, 1942.

[25]Named from Devonshire, England, where there are typical exposures. Sedgwick, A., and Murchison, R. I., Geol. Soc. London Proc., vol. 3, pp. 121-123, abstract, 1839.

[36]Named for Wapsipinicon River, Iowa, along which the typical locality occurs between Troy Mills and Central City. Norton, W. H., The geology of Linn County: Iowa Geol. Survey, vol. 4, p. 155, 1894.

[37]Workman, L. E., *op cit.*, p. 197.

[38]Named for Cedar Valley in southeastern Iowa. McGee, W. J., The Pleistocene history of northeastern Iowa—the indurated rocks: U. S. Geol. Survey Ann. Rept., vol. 11, p. 319, 1891.

or the Lingle limestone, above the Grand Tower, in southern Illinois.[39]

MISSISSIPPIAN SYSTEM[40]

The Mississippian system in Illinois is divided into the Iowa and Chester series, and the Iowa series is divided into the Kinderhook, Osage, and Meramec groups, from the base upwards. Most of the thickest and most conspicuous Mississippian formations are in the Iowa series.

IOWA SERIES[41]

KINDERHOOK GROUP[42]

GRASSY CREEK FORMATION[43]

The Grassy Creek formation is preponderantly a dark brown to black shale, with grayish-green to gray strata. Some of the shale is slightly calcareous and micaceous, and pyrite crystals and concretions are common. Plant spores, *Tasmanites huronensis* (Dawson) S. W. and B. (formerly *Sporangites huronense*), are common fossils.

The shale ranges from 50 to 105 feet in thickness, the thickness increasing from southwest to northeast. On the basis of its stratigraphic position, the Grassy Creek shale is usually considered to be in the Kinderhook group at the base of the Mississippian system, but some geologists believe it is Upper Devonian.[44]

LOUISIANA FORMATION[45]

The Louisiana limestone has been recognized in the Carlinville quadrangle only in the Chrysler-Hall No. 1 well, in which it was described by the driller as a brown limestone 8 feet thick. It is usually light gray

to buff and dense or lithographic. Like the Grassy Creek shale, the Louisiana limestone is usually considered as Mississippian in age, but some geologists believe it to be Devonian.[44]

HANNIBAL FORMATION[46]

In the Carlinville quadrangle the Hannibal formation consists of the Hamburg and Maple Mill members.

Hamburg Member[47]

The Hamburg member of the Hannibal formation is predominantly a siltstone and shale with a subordinate amount of oolitic limestone interbedded with siltstone. The shale and siltstone is usually light gray to gray, subordinately brownish gray to brown. The oolitic limestone is slightly dolomitic, commonly gray or buff, and consists of somewhat coarse gray-centered oolites in a groundmass of fine texture.

The thickness of the Hamburg member ranges from 72 to 87 feet in the quadrangle. It is separated from the underlying Louisiana limestone by a sharp unconformity, but is conformable with the overlying Maple Mill shale.

On paleontological evidence the Hamburg member is about the equivalent of the Glen Park[48] member of the Sulphur Springs (basal Mississippian) formation of Missouri, and the two formations are thought by some[49] to be identical. Subsurface investigations have shown that east of Macoupin County the Hamburg member grades laterally into the New Albany shale, making a part of that shale of Hannibal age.

Maple Mill Member[50]

The Maple Mill member of the Hannibal formation is usually a slightly calcareous shale, but in the Phillips-Giller No. 1 well it is a siltstone, 23 feet thick, with a little

[39]Workman, L. E., *op. cit.*, p. 197.
[40]So named because the system is characteristically developed in the Mississippi Valley. Winchell, A., On the geological age and equivalents of the Marshall group: Amer. Philos. Proc., vol. 11, p. 79, 1869; pp. 245 and 385, 1870.
[41]Named for the state of Iowa. Weller, Stuart, The Chester series in Illinois: Jour. Geol., vol. 28, p. 282, 1920.
[42]Named for the village of Kinderhook, Pike County, Ill. Meek, F. B., and Worthen, A. H., Remarks on the age of the goniatite limestone at Rockford, Indiana, etc.: Am. Jour. Sci., 2d series, vol. 32, pp. 167-177, 1861; Note to the paper of Meek and Worthen, same vol., p. 288.
[43]Named for Grassy Creek, Pike County, Mo. Keyes, C. R., Iowa Acad. Sci. Proc., vol. 5, pp. 59-63, 1898.
[44]Branson, E. B., "Devonian of northeastern Missouri," in Illinois Geol. Survey Bull. 68, pp. 174-181, 1944.
[45]Named for Louisiana, Mo. Keyes, C. R., The principal Mississippian section: Geol. Soc. Amer. Bull., vol. 3, p. 289, 1892.

[46]Named for Hannibal, Mo. Keyes, C. R., *op. cit.*, p. 289.
[47]Named for Hamburg, Calhoun County, Ill. Weller, Stuart, Kinderhook faunal studies: St. Louis Acad. Sci. Trans., vol. 16, pp. 464-467, 1906.
[48]Weller, Stuart, *op. cit.*, p. 467.
[49]Wilmarth, Grace, Lexicon of geologic names of the United States: U. S. Geol. Surv. Bull. 896, pt. 1, p. 899, 1938.
[50]The basal shales of the Kinderhook group in Iowa, typically exposed in Burlington, Iowa, and along English River, were called the Maple Mill shale. Bain, H. F., Central Iowa section of the Mississippian series: Amer. Geologist, vol. 15, p. 322, 1895.

silty limestone, and about nine miles north of the Phillips-Giller well, the uppermost 50 feet of the combined Hamburg-Maple Mill unit is a siltstone with some micaceous gray shale. In the Lagers-Bristow well there are a few feet of light buff fine-grained very silty limestone. The Maple Mill silt-stone is usually calcareous and gray, light gray, or pale greenish gray, and the shale is calcareous, sometimes silty, and greenish gray.

The Maple Mill member ranges from 15 to 36 feet in thickness in the quadrangle. It is conformable both with the Hamburg member below and with the Chouteau formation above.

CHOUTEAU FORMATION[51]

The Chouteau formation is the upper-most formation of the Kinderhook group. It occurs only in the extreme southern part of the Carlinville quadrangle, where it is reported to be 23 feet thick. It thickens to the south and west.[52]

The Chouteau formation is a limestone, locally dolomitic and less commonly silty and glauconitic. It ranges from light gray to gray or brownish gray. Its texture commonly is dense and lithographic or sublithographic, but in some places it becomes somewhat coarsely crystalline.

The Chouteau formation rests with apparent conformity on the Maple Mill member,[53] but its absence north of the south part of the Carlinville quadrangle seems to point to unconformable relations with the overlying Osage group. It can be traced directly into the Rockford limestone of Indiana, and there is evidence that it is contemporaneous with the McCraney[53] limestone of western Illinois. It also has been correlated with the North Hill member of the Hampden formation of Iowa.[54]

OSAGE GROUP[55]

Originally the Osage group consisted only of the Burlington and Keokuk formations, but it now includes the Fern Glen, Burlington, Keokuk, and Warsaw formations.[56]

FERN GLEN FORMATION[57]

The Fern Glen formation is principally cherty limestone, slightly silty or dolomitic, with some dolomite, shale, and siltstone. It ranges from white through light gray and pale grayish green to gray and green and is fine- to medium-grained or coarsely crystalline. The shale, which is most common at the base or in the lower part of the formation, is commonly red but may be reddish brown and green. The chert occurs in white, pink, and pale green nodules.

The Fern Glen formation varies considerably in thickness in a southeast direction, from 56 feet in the northwest portion of the quadrangle to 127 feet in the southeast corner. It lies unconformably on the Kinderhook formations, generally on the Maple Mill shale in the north part of the quadrangle and vicinity and invariably on the Chouteau formation in the south part of the quadrangle and farther south. In western Illinois there is locally an angular discordance between the Chouteau and the Fern Glen formations,[58] but the relationships between the two formations in the quadrangle and vicinity point either to nondeposition of the Chouteau or to its erosion after deposition.

The Carlinville quadrangle is about 60 miles from the type area of the Fern Glen formation, but the correlation of the formation within the quadrangle is established by general stratigraphic position and by lithological similarities.

[51]Named for Chouteau Springs, Mo. Swallow, G. C., First and Second Annual Reports: Geol. Survey of Missouri, pp. 101-103, 1855.
[52]Workman, L. E. and Gillette, Tracy, Subsurface stratigraphy of the Kinderhook-New Albany strata in Illinois: unpublished manuscript, Illinois Geol. Survey.
[53]Workman and Gillette, op. cit.
[54]Moore, R. C., The Mississippian system in the Upper Mississippi Valley region: Guidebook of Ninth Annual Field Conference, Kansas Geol. Soc., p. 241, 1935.
[55]Named for Osage River, Mo. Williams, H. S., Correlation papers, Devonian and Carboniferous: U. S. Geol. Survey Bull. 80, p. 265, 1891.
[56]Some geologists prefer to classify the Warsaw formation in the Meramec group.
[57]Named for Fern Glen station, Mo., on the Missouri Pacific Railroad, near which the typical locality is in a railroad cut in the bluff of the Meramec River. Weller, Stuart, The fauna of the Fern Glen formation: Geol. Soc. Amer. Bull., vol. 20, p. 266, 1909.
[58]Moore, R. C., The Mississippian system in the Upper Mississippi Valley region: Guidebook of the Ninth Annual Field Conference, Kansas Geol. Soc., p. 241, 1935.

BURLINGTON AND KEOKUK FORMATIONS[59]

The Burlington and Keokuk formations are treated as a single unit. The rocks are cherty limestones. Strata of pure dolomite are rare but many of the beds are dolomitic. They are commonly light gray or white but occasionally buff, and range from fine-grained to coarse-grained. Some of the samples contain glauconite and locally the samples are fossiliferous. The chert is white and opaque to translucent, or dense-textured and dull-colored.

The Burlington and Keokuk formations in this region are generally 175 to 190 feet thick, but toward the southeast corner of the Carlinville quadrangle the thickness decreases to a minimum of 123 feet. The formations are conformable with each other, and the base of the Burlington formation rests conformably on the Fern Glen, in some places with hardly any lithological distinction. The persistent limestone of the Keokuk formation is in lithologic contrast to the overlying Warsaw shale, but there is no evidence of an unconformity between them.

WARSAW FORMATION[60]

The Warsaw formation is predominantly a shale, but siltstone, sandstone, limestone, dolomitic limestone, and dolomite also occur in it. The shales are calcareous and/or micaceous, are light gray or gray, and locally contain macerated fossils and recognizable quartz geodes. Considerable glauconite imparts a greenish color to some of the beds.

The limestone is buff and coarsely crystalline, with greenish shale partings. Some of the limestone contains black chert nodules, but white chert also occurs.

The Warsaw formation thickens from 75 to 100 feet along the west edge to 135 to 150 feet along the east edge of the Carlinville quadrangle. Southwest of the quadrangle it is only 60 feet thick. This formation is conformable on the Keokuk formation. Local unconformities above the

Warsaw in western Illinois have been noted,[61] but there is no evidence of an unconformity in the Carlinville quadrangle.

MERAMEC GROUP[62]

In Illinois Geological Survey usage the Meramec group includes the Salem, St. Louis, and Ste. Genevieve formations.

SALEM FORMATION[63]

The Salem formation consists of limestone and dolomite. The limestone is commonly buff to light and medium brown and some is light gray, frequently showing mottling. The dolomite is buff and light gray to brown. Both limestone and dolomite are crystalline, fine- to coarse-grained. Chert is present in the upper third to half of the formation. The formation is highly fossiliferous; the foraminifer *Endothyra* and bryozoa are commonly recognized.

The thickness of the Salem formation in the Carlinville quadrangle ranges between 111 and 148 feet. It is conformable both with the Warsaw formation below and with the St. Louis formation above. Locally its contact with the underlying Warsaw formation is gradational[64] and its upper part resembles the St. Louis formation, which makes the contacts generally difficult to recognize except on a faunal basis. Species of *Endothyra* are cited as good markers for the Salem formation.[65]

ST. LOUIS FORMATION[66]

The St. Louis formation is chiefly a limestone, although some dolomite is almost always present. The limestone commonly is light gray to gray, occasionally buff or brown. It is lithographic to very fine- and fine-grained with some medium-sized grains frequently scattered in the finer groundmass.

[59]Named for the towns of Burlington and Keokuk, Iowa, respectively. Hall, James, Observations on the Carboniferous limestones of the Mississippi Valley: Amer. Jour. Sci. and Arts, 2nd ser., vol. 23, p. 190, 1857.

[60]Named for Warsaw, Ill. Hall, James, *op. cit.*, p. 191.

[61]Moore, R. C., *op cit.*, pp. 244-245.

[62]Named after Meramec River in Missouri. Ulrich, E. O., Determination and correlation of formations: U. S. Geol. Survey Prof. Paper 24, table facing p. 90, 1904.

[63]Named for Salem, Ind. Cummings, E. R., The use of Bedford as a formational term: Jour. Geol., vol. 9, p. 233, 1901.

[64]Collingwood, D. M., Oil and gas possibilities of parts of Jersey, Greene, and Madison counties: Illinois Geol. Survey Rept. Inv. 30, pp. 24, 26, 1933.

[65]Henbest, Lloyd G., *Endothyra baileyi:* Shimer, H. W., and Shrock, R. R., Index fossils of North America, New York, pp. 15-16, 1944.

[66]Named for St. Louis, Mo. Engelmann, G., Remarks on the St. Louis limestone: Am. Jour. Sci., 2nd ser., vol. 3, pp. 119-120, 1847.

In some localities it is oolitic, and chert occurs very commonly. Fossils are not abundant. In the Lagers-Bristow No. 1 well there is an intraformational conglomerate, a common feature of the St. Louis formation.

The dolomite beds are similar to the limestones. They contain chert, some of them are slightly silty, and commonly they are light gray to light brown or brown. Very fine-grained textures prevail, and in some instances there is a vesicular texture.

Anhydrite occurs relatively near the base of the formation in four wells southeast of the quadrangle. Anhydrite is found extensively in the St. Louis formation in Iowa.[67]

The St. Louis formation thickens eastward from 125 feet along the west edge to 225 feet or more along the east edge of the Carlinville quadrangle. Still farther east, the thickness reaches 302 feet.

The St. Louis limestone lies conformably on the Salem formation, but there is an unconformity between it and the Ste. Genevieve limestone which in normal sequence lies above the St. Louis formation.[68] At some localities in and around the Carlinville quadrangle all the Mississippian formations above the St. Louis formation are missing and beds of the Pennsylvanian system lie directly on it.

STE. GENEVIEVE FORMATION[69]

The Ste. Genevieve formation occurs in only two of the wells in the Carlinville quadrangle. It is commonly a light gray, buff, or white, silty, sandy, or oolitic limestone. There are occasional dolomites, and in both limestone and dolomite the texture is very fine- to medium-grained. The thickness of the formation in the wells in which it occurs ranges between 9 and 32 feet.

Unconformities occur both between the Ste. Genevieve formation and the St. Louis formation below[68] and between the Ste.

Genevieve formation and the Chester series that normally overlies it.[70] Also, because in much of the quadrangle and surrounding area the Chester series is missing, beds of the Pennsylvanian system lie directly on the Ste. Genevieve formation.

CHESTER SERIES[71]

The rocks of the Chester series generally may be described as "alternating sandstone and limestone-shale formations that . . . fall naturally into pairs. In general, each sandstone is separated from the underlying limestone-shale formation by a minor but probably widespread unconformity, but passes more or less gradually into the limestone-shale formation above."[72]

Strata belonging to the Chester series apparently do not commonly occur in the Carlinville quadrangle. A 13-foot bed of a pale greenish-gray very fine-grained slightly micaceous argillaceous sandstone that occurs in the Hayes-Alderson No. 1 well in the SE¼ SE¼ NE¼ sec. 17, T. 12 N., R. 7 W. (North Otter Twp.) has been tentatively identified as part of the Aux Vases formation.[73] What is believed to be the same formation increases in thickness to as much as 30 feet in wells east of the quadrangle.

In the Standard Oil Company test well in the NE corner of sec. 9, T. 10 N., R. 6 W. (Shaw Point Twp.), there are 26 feet of green shale with nodules, streaks, and lenses of limestone that are also provisionally classified as of Chester age and may be representative of either or both the Renault[74] and the Paint Creek formations.[75] Strata assigned to these formations are found in wells east and south of the Carlinville quadrangle.

[67]Wilder, Frank A., Gypsum; its occurrence, origin, technology, and uses: Iowa Geol. Survey Rept., vol. 28, pp. 163-164, 1919.
[68]Weller, Stuart and St. Clair, Stuart, Geology of Ste. Genevieve County, Missouri: Missouri Bur. Geol. and Mines, vol. 22, 2nd series, p. 221, 1928.
[69]Named for Ste. Genevieve, Mo. Shumard, B. F., Observations on the geology of Ste. Genevieve county: St. Louis Acad. Sci. Trans., vol. 1, p. 406, 1859.

[70]Weller, J. Marvin, and Sutton, A. H., Mississippian border of Eastern Interior Basin: Bull. Amer. Assn. Petr. Geol., vol. 24, pp. 819-822, 1940. Reprinted as Illinois Geol. Survey Rept. Inv. 62.
[71]Named for Chester, Ill. Worthen, A. H., The geology of Illinois: Geol. Survey of Illinois, vol. 1, pp. 40, 77, 1866.
[72]Weller, J. Marvin, Geology and oil possibilities of extreme southern Illinois: Illinois Geol. Survey Rept. Inv. 71, p. 31, 1940.
[73]Named for Aux Vases River, Mo. Keyes, C. R., Geol. Soc. Amer. Bull., vol. 3, p. 295, 1892.
[74]Named for Renault Township, Monroe County, Ill. Weller, Stuart, Stratigraphy of the Chester group in southwestern Illinois: Ill. Acad. Sci. Trans., vol. 6, p. 123, 1913.
[75]Named for Paint Creek, Monroe County, Ill. Weller, Stuart, op. cit., p. 126.

Chester strata may be present elsewhere in the quadrangle, but they have not been identified in any of the other wells for which records but no samples are available. The maximum thickness of the Chester series within a few miles of the Carlinville quadrangle is 50 feet.

There are important unconformities both between the Chester series and the underlying Ste. Genevieve formation (the top formation of the Iowa series) and between the Chester series and the overlying Pennsylvanian system. The magnitude of the latter unconformity is indicated by the fact that much or all of the Chester series is lacking in the area. In addition there are lesser unconformities between some pairs of the Chester formations, but these are of course not evident in the quadrangle.

CHAPTER IV — PENNSYLVANIAN[1] STRATIGRAPHY

The Pennsylvanian system underlies the Carlinville quadrangle. It consists of shales, underclays, coals, sandstones, limestones, and siltstones that occur in frequently repeated sequences. The basal strata rest unconformably on rocks of the Mississippian system. The maximum thickness reported in the quadrangle is 602 feet. The variabilities in thickness are many and erratic, but the thickness tends to increase to the south and east. Many of the variabilities in thickness are due to the irregular Mississippian surface on which the Pennsylvanian strata lie.

In Illinois the Pennsylvanian system is divided into the Caseyville, Tradewater, Carbondale, and McLeansboro groups.[2] These groups are comprised of repeated sequences of strata, called cyclothems (fig. 6).[3] Many of the individual lithologic units in the cyclothems are sufficiently thick, sufficiently distinctive, or sufficiently important economically that they have been given names. The current classification of the Pennsylvanian strata definitely known or believed to be present in the Carlinville quadrangle is given in the tabulation (p. 21).

The lower part of each cyclothem (units 1-6, inclusive, fig. 6) appears to have been deposited generally in a nonmarine environment, whereas the upper part (units 6-10, inclusive, fig. 6) was deposited under marine conditions. The cyclothem represents a succession of geologic events that was repeated many times throughout the Pennsylvanian period, and the character of the respective lithologic units is very much the same in all cyclothems.

GENERAL LITHOLOGIC UNITS

The following description is taken from Illinois Geological Survey Bulletin 66, pp. 90-92, modified to set forth the lithologic aspects prevailing in the Carlinville quadrangle.

1. *Sandstone.* — The basal sandstones are silty and many are clayey. They commonly grade both laterally and vertically to sandy shale or siltstone. Mica may be abundant, especially along the bedding planes. Carbonaceous matter and iron oxide are abundant, coloring the sandstone accordingly.

The sandstones are massive locally and are thin-bedded elsewhere, and not uncommonly the two extremes are interlayered. Individual beds as much as 5 feet thick are common, especially in the filled channels. Although they are locally noncalcareous, most of the sandstones contain a small amount of calcium carbonate irregularly scattered through them. In the upper cyclothems in the Carlinville quadrangle the basal units are commonly micaceous red or yellow slightly sandy shale.

2. *Sandy shale.*—The basal sandstones usually grade upward into gray sandy shales, which in turn frequently grade upward into the underclays. This unit is poorly defined in the Carlinville quadrangle.

3. *Limestone.*—The lowermost of the three limestones in the ideal cyclothem occurs at the base or in the lower part of the underclays and is fine-textured, compact, and light gray. Many of them weather whitish. They are usually argillaceous, and commonly all or parts of them grade laterally to a discontinuous layer of rough-surfaced, irregular nodules in clay. Occasionally there are many fossils, usually of organisms that lived in brackish or fresh water.

4. *Underclay.* — The underclays are mostly medium gray except in the upper few inches, which is dark gray or nearly black. The fracture surfaces through several inches of the clay immediately below the topmost clay are commonly stained brown with limonite. The underclays are not bedded, although traces of bedding planes may occur near the base where they

[1]Named for the state of Pennsylvania. Williams, H. S., The geology of Washington County: Arkansas Geol. Survey Ann. Rept. for 1888. vol. 4, p. xiii. 1891.
[2]Willman, H. B., and Payne, J. N., Geology and mineral resources of the Marseilles, Ottawa, and Streator quadrangles: Illinois Geol. Survey Bull. 66, pp. 85-87, 1942.
[3]Wanless, H. R., and Weller, J. Marvin, Correlation and extent of Pennsylvanian cyclothems: Bull. Geol. Soc. Amer., vol. 43, p. 1003, 1932.

PENNSYLVANIAN STRATA

Group	Cyclothem	Distinctive units or characteristic lithologic features
	25. McWain sandstone.....	A channel sandstone with a few thin discontinuous stringers of coal.
	24. Shoal Creek..........	Includes a thick limestone
	23. Macoupin............	Ledgemaking limestone, weathering brick red; No. 9 coal.
	22. Burroughs beds.......	Coarse-grained limestone with Productids; strata conspicuously sandy.
	21. Carlinville...........	Conspicuous well-bedded dense limestone, weathering brown.
McLeansboro......	20. Trivoli..............	Conspicuously shaly; close-set vertical joint fractures in shale; No. 8 coal.
	19. Scottville...........	Locally highly fossiliferous limestone.
	18. Gimlet..............	Limestone
	17. Sparland............	Piasa limestone; thick shale above No. 7 coal.
	16. Jamestown or Bankston Fork..............	Limestone
	15. Brereton............	Brereton limestone; No. 6 coal; Vermilionville sandstone.
	14. St. David...........	Canton shale; No. 5 coal.
Carbondale........	13. Summum............	Hanover limestone; No. 4 coal; Pleasantview sandstone.
	12. Liverpool...........	Purington shale; Lowell coal; Oak Grove limestone; Francis Creek shale; Colchester (No. 2) coal.
	11. Abingdon...........	
	10. Greenbush..........	
	9. Wiley...............	
Tradewater........	8. Seahorne............	Seahorne limestone
	7. Upper DeLong.......	
	6. Middle DeLong......	
	5. Lower DeLong.......	
	4. Seville..............	Rock Island (No. 1) coal; Bernadotte sandstone.
	3. Pope Creek..........	
Caseyville.........	2. Tartar	
	1. Babylon	

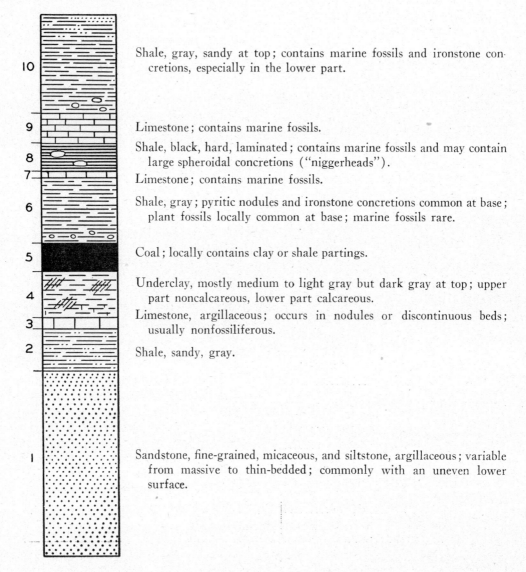

Shale, gray, sandy at top; contains marine fossils and ironstone concretions, especially in the lower part.

Limestone; contains marine fossils.

Shale, black, hard, laminated; contains marine fossils and may contain large spheroidal concretions ("niggerheads").

Limestone; contains marine fossils.

Shale, gray; pyritic nodules and ironstone concretions common at base; plant fossils locally common at base; marine fossils rare.

Coal; locally contains clay or shale partings.

Underclay, mostly medium to light gray but dark gray at top; upper part noncalcareous, lower part calcareous.

Limestone, argillaceous; occurs in nodules or discontinuous beds; usually nonfossiliferous.

Shale, sandy, gray.

Sandstone, fine-grained, micaceous, and siltstone, argillaceous; variable from massive to thin-bedded; commonly with an uneven lower surface.

FIG. 6.—An ideally complete cyclothem.   (From Illinois Geol. Survey Bull. 66, fig. 42.)

grade into the underlying shale or sandstone. Many of the underclays fracture along smooth slickensided surfaces which extend in all directions through the underclay but are rarely as much as six inches long. The upper part of the underclays is usually noncalcareous and the lower part calcareous, but in some cases the entire unit is noncalcareous.

5. *Coal.*—The coal beds are composed of interlaminated brilliant bands of vitrain and bright bands of clarain in varying proportions, with lesser amounts of fusain in thin lenses and small fragments. The coal breaks readily parallel to the bedding at fusain and clay partings. Also it tends to fracture along vertical joints, but the vertical jointing, or cleat, is not well developed, causing large lumps of broken coal to be irregular in shape.

All the coal contains pyrite, as stony or earthy pyrite between the coal layers, as nodular concretionary masses or minute crystals within the coal layers, or as veinlike fillings in vertical cracks across the bedding. Calcite also occurs in thin veinlike fillings.

6. *Shale.*—Two types of gray or greenish-gray shale, both among the less common units in the cyclothems, may separate the coal from overlying limestone or black shale. The lower locally contains plant fossils and usually lacks fossils of marine invertebrates, and apparently is the top member of the nonmarine part of the cyclothem. The upper of the two shales is similar but is thin-bedded and calcareous and contains marine fossils; it marks the initial deposit of the marine part of the cyclothem. It is usually less than 5 feet thick.

7. *Limestone.*—The middle limestone of the cyclothem is a black argillaceous limestone or calcareous shale, usually crowded with whitish fossils and usually less than two inches thick. It is present in only a few cyclothems but in these it is a persistent bed.

8. *Shale.*—The hard black shale, called "slate" by coal miners, occurs in very thin uniform beds along which it can be split into large sheets. When soaked in water,

it does not soften and become plastic like the gray shales. It contains much organic matter. At some horizons small spherical concretions flex the beds and produce a pustulate appearance. Large black limestone or ironstone concretions, called "niggerheads," are also common, and the shale is locally contorted where these are abundant. The black shale usually has sharp contacts with the adjacent limestone units, but where the uppermost limestone is missing the black shale grades into the overlying gray shale through a zone in which the hardness decreases, the beds become thicker, and the color becomes lighter. Locally the black shale is medium- to thick-bedded and has a blocky fracture. In several cyclothems it is soft and mottled black and gray or greenish gray. Marine fossils are locally abundant, and some of the black shales of the Carlinville quadrangle locally have an abundant conodont fauna.

9. *Limestone.*—The uppermost limestone is usually the thickest and most continuous limestone in the cyclothem. It is often a massive single ledge of fine-grained light gray limestone which weathers to shades of brown or red. It may be thin-bedded or consist of several beds separated by shale. In some cyclothems it is nodular and separates into rounded aggregates when weathered. Many beds are argillaceous but a few are not. The limestone commonly is fine-grained. Crinoidal beds are locally present and marine fossils are common.

10. *Shale.*—The topmost member of the cyclothem is a shale, gray or greenish gray, except in the lower few feet where it is dark gray or bluish gray. It is usually the thickest shale in the cyclothem, although locally it is exceeded in thickness by the shale overlying the coal. The lower 2 to 5 feet of these top shales is thin-bedded, above which the beds are mostly 1/4 inch to 2 inches thick. Discoidal concretions of limestone and "ironstone" are common, especially in the lower 5 feet, and they seem to occur in definite horizons. The "ironstone" concretions are largely sideritic (iron carbonate) mixed with a little clay and in some cases with calcium carbonate. Where the shales are thick the upper part is sandy and

locally contains thin beds of sandstone. Marine fossils occur in the lower part of the shale.

Although the respective lithologic units are similar in all cyclothems, usually one or more of them in each cyclothem has some distinctive characteristic, or there are some peculiarities in the succession within the cyclothem by which almost every cyclothem can be recognized and identified, at least locally. In some cases, distinctive characteristics, even of a very thin lithologic unit, may prevail over extensive areas, so that correlation of such beds, the including cyclothem, and other cyclothems may be made across considerable distances.

Even though a complete cyclothem may be present, it is practically impossible to identify all its constituent lithologic units in drillers' well records or even in samples of well cuttings. Only in cases where cores of test borings are available for study can the complete succession of strata and cyclothems be positively identified. However, in many cases some of the units which have distinctive characteristics can be more or less definitely identified in well records or in samples, and thus their presence and position can be determined. Some of such beds that appear in wells in the Carlinville quadrangle are herewith discussed.[4]

CASEYVILLE GROUP[5]

Four deep wells in the quadrangle, the Phillips-Giller No. 1 in the NW 1/4 sec. 15, T. 11 N., R. 8 W. (South Palmyra Twp.), the Lagers-Bristow No. 1 in the NE 1/4 sec. 7, T. 11 N., R. 7 W. (South Otter Twp.), the Pummill-Monetti No. 1 in the SE 1/4 sec. 20, T. 10 N., R. 7 W. (Carlinville Twp.), just northwest of Carlinville, and the Turner-Chamness No. 1 in sec. 4, T. 9 N., R. 6 W. (Honey Point Twp.), have at the base of the Pennsylvanian succession a thick sandstone (50 feet thick in the Turner-Chamness well), which may be the Caseyville sandstone.

TRADEWATER GROUP[6]

Of the cyclothems and strata comprising the Tradewater group in the Carlinville quadrangle, only the No. 1 coal in the Seville cyclothem, the Seahorne limestone in the Seahorne cyclothem, and the Medora coal in the Wiley cyclothem can be identified in the wells.

SEVILLE CYCLOTHEM[7]

The Seville cyclothem contains the Rock Island (No. 1) coal, which is the lowest Pennsylvanian stratum that may be recognized with any assurance in wells in the Carlinville quadrangle. It is represented by coal about 2 to 2 1/2 feet thick in the Lagers-Bristow No. 1 well (NE 1/4 sec. 7, T. 11 N., R. 7 W., South Otter Twp.) and in the Goodman Reinecke No. 1 well (SE 1/4 sec. 17, T. 10 N., R. 7 W., Carlinville Twp.), 40 feet above the base of the Pennsylvanian system and respectively 150 and 130 feet below the top of the Seahorne limestone.

SEAHORNE CYCLOTHEM[8]

This cyclothem in its typical development comprises, in ascending order, sandstone, underclay, coal, shale, and marine limestone and is about 12 feet thick. To the south and east it probably thickens, as the limestone alone ranges from 5 to 15 feet thick in the Carlinville quadrangle. In only one of the wells in the quadrangle, the Bridge-Feiker No. 1 well (SW 1/4 sec. 1, T. 9 N., R. 7 W., Brushy Mound Twp.), is there a coal under the limestone.

The Seahorne limestone has been recognized tentatively in at least 14 of the deeper wells of the Carlinville quadrangle, which are distributed in a broad belt from the northwest to the southeast parts of the quadrangle.

---

[4]Records of a few wells in the quadrangle are published in Appendix B; records of all wells are available for reference and loan at the Illinois State Geological Survey.

[5]Named for Caseyville, Union County, Ky., near which it is exposed. Glenn, L. C., The geology of Webster County: Kentucky Geol. Survey Rept. Prog., p. 27, 1910 and 1911.

[6]Named for Tradewater River, east of Battery Rock, Ky., along which it is exposed. Glenn, L. C., *op. cit.*, p. 27.

[7]Named for Seville, Fulton County, Ill. Wanless, H. R., Pennsylvanian correlations in the Eastern Interior and Appalachian coal fields: Geol. Soc. Amer. Spec. Paper 17, p. 101, 1939. Wanless, H. R., Pennsylvanian cycles in western Illinois: *in* Illinois Geol. Survey Bull. 60, pp. 179-193, 1931.

[8]Named for Seahorne branch, Fulton County, Ill. Wanless, H. R., Geol. Soc. Amer. Spec. Paper 17, p. 101, 1939. Wanless, H. R., *in* Illinois Geol. Survey Bull. 60, pp. 179-193, 1931.

In the northwest part of the quadrangle it is light in color, ranging from white through light gray and buff to brownish gray and brown, but in the southeast part of the quadrangle it is dark or black and is pyritic in a few instances. It usually is finely to very finely crystalline but occasionally is coarsely crystalline. Its average thickness is about 10 feet, but in the Lagers-Bristow and the Hayes-Alderson wells, in the north part of the quadrangle, its thickness is reported to be 20 feet.

WILEY CYCLOTHEM[9]

The coal of the Wiley cyclothem, also called the Medora coal,[10] occurs in five of the deep borings in the Carlinville quadrangle, namely the Northwestern Macoupin Coal Company test, NE ¼ sec. 4, T. 11 N., R. 8 W. (South Palmyra Twp.), the A. Braun test No. 2, and the Mudgett-Goebelt Nos. 7 and 8 wells, all in the SW ¼ sec. 20, and the Walker-Kirchkoff well in the NW ¼ sec. 35, T. 10 N., R. 7 W. (Carlinville Twp.). The coal averages about 3 feet in thickness. In the Northwestern Macoupin Coal Company test, 3 feet of clay and shale that according to the driller's report lies under the coal may represent a part of the underclay that is characteristic of the cyclothem in Illinois and Iowa.[11]

CARBONDALE GROUP[12]

Nearly all the shallow test borings in the Carlinville quadrangle penetrated the No. 6 coal; thus the beds of the Brereton cyclothem down through at least part of the underclay are reported in practically every record in the quadrangle, and several of the deeper borings penetrated additional strata of the Carbondale group.

LIVERPOOL CYCLOTHEM[13]

The Liverpool cyclothem includes many strata of sufficient importance to have been named. In ascending order, the units of the cyclothem are the Isabel sandstone, an underclay, Colchester (No. 2) coal, Francis Creek shale, black laminated shale, Oak Grove group of fossiliferous thin limestones and dark shales, and Purington shale. In its typical locality the cyclothem is about 90 feet thick,[14] and in the Carlinville quadrangle it ranges from 85 to 102 feet.

What is believed to be the Isabel[15] or basal sandstone of the Liverpool cyclothem is reported in the records of the Hayes-Alderson and the Turner-Chamness wells. The sandstone is from 15 to 20 feet thick, slightly shaly, micaceous and carbonaceous, fine- to very fine-grained, and grayish. In several of the other well records which show the Colchester (No. 2) coal, the coal is underlain by gray sandy shales or shaly sandstones which also may be the Isabel sandstone.

The underclay of the Liverpool cyclothem cannot be differentiated from other shale listed in the well records.

The Colchester (No. 2) coal, tentatively identified in the records of 8 borings, averages nearly 4 feet in thickness and lies at an average distance of about 82 feet below the Herrin (No. 6) coal.

A blue or gray shale about 40 feet thick in two wells and a "slate" 92 feet thick in one well are identified as the Purington shale. None of the other members of the Liverpool cyclothem can be definitely recognized in the records of wells in the quadrangle.

SUMMUM CYCLOTHEM[16]

In its typical locality in western Illinois the Summum cyclothem includes, in as-

[9]Named for the Wiley School, Deerfield Township, Fulton County, Ill. Wanless, H. R., Geol. Soc. Amer. Spec Paper 17, p. 108, 1939. Wanless, H. R., *in* Illinois Geol. Survey Bull. 60, pp. 179-193, 1931.

[10]Payne, J. N., Structure of Herrin (No. 6) coal bed in Macoupin County, etc.: Illinois Geol. Survey Circ. 88, p. 3, 1942.

[11]Weller, J. M., Wanless, H. R., Cline, L. M., and Stookey, D. G., Interbasin Pennsylvanian correlations, Illinois and Iowa: Bull. Amer. Assoc. Petr. Geol., vol. 26, p. 1589, 1942.

[12]Named for Carbondale in Jackson County, Ill. Shaw, E. W. and Savage, T. E., U. S. Geol Survey Atlas, Murphysboro-Herrin folio (No. 185), p. 6, 1912.

[13]Named for Liverpool Township, Fulton County, Ill. Wanless, H. R., *in* Illinois Geol. Survey Bull. 60, pp. 179-193, 1931. Willman, H. B. and Payne, J. N., Illinois Geol. Survey Bull. 66, footnote 36, p. 95, 1942.

[14]Wanless, H. R., Pennsylvanian cycles in western Illinois: Illinois Geol. Survey Bull. 60, fig. 46, p. 192, 1931.

[15]Named for Isabel Township, Fulton County, Ill. Wanless, H. R., Geol. Soc. Amer. Spec. Paper 17, p. 87, 1939. Wanless, H. R., *in* Illinois Geol. Survey Bull. 60, pp. 179-193, 1931.

[16]Named for the town of Summum in southern Fulton County, Ill. Wanless, H. R., Geol. Soc. Amer. Spec. Paper 17, p. 103, 1939. Wanless, H. R., *in* Illinois Geol. Survey Bull. 60, p. 182, 1931.

cending order, Pleasantview sandstone, sandy shale, limestone, underclay, No. 4 coal, black shale, and Hanover limestone.[17] The lowermost 57 feet of strata in the No. 2 mine shaft of the Standard Oil Company appears to represent the entire cyclothem in the Carlinville quadrangle, recorded in unusual detail:

	Thickness in feet
Limestone	1¾
Shale	3⅓
Limestone, shaly	2
Shale, gray	3⅙
"Slate," black	3
Coal	½
"Fireclay"	5
Sandstone	5
Shale, sandy, dark	1
Sandstone	6
Sandstone, shaly	19

This succession is almost identical with the Summum cyclothem in northern Illinois.[18]

The Summum cyclothem has also been identified tentatively in 7 other borings in the quadrangle; additional borings doubtless penetrated the cyclothem, but the strata are not described in sufficient detail to be satisfactorily identified as such.

The cyclothem ranges from 50 to 65 feet in thickness.

The Pleasantview[19] sandstone, the basal member of the Summum cyclothem, appears in all the records where the Summum cyclothem has been recognized. It ranges from 32 to 72 feet and averages 48 feet in thickness. The sandstone is micaceous, in some cases slightly silty or carbonaceous, light gray, gray, or greenish gray, ordinarily very fine- to fine-grained, but in a few instances coarse grains appear. A marked feature of the unit is an abundance of sideritic nodules.

In addition to the limestone reported in the Standard Oil No. 2 mine shaft, which is separated from the No. 4 coal beneath it by 6 feet of black and gray shale, a limestone 10 feet thick in the C. Hauer No. 1 well, NW ¼ sec. 25, T. 10 N., R. 7 W., is believed to be the Hanover limestone, as

a shale 10 feet thick separates it from the underclay and St. David (?) limestone successively beneath the Herrin (No. 6) coal.

ST. DAVID CYCLOTHEM[20]

The St. David cyclothem in western Illinois contains the Springfield (No. 5) coal bed and the thick Canton shale but does not have a conspicuous sandstone at its base. Hardly any strata which might be assigned to the St. David cyclothem appear in the well records of the Carlinville quadrangle. The Springfield (No. 5) coal, which is persistent and 5 to 6 feet thick in north-central and northwestern Illinois, is not recorded, and without it the St. David cyclothem cannot be definitely recognized. However, a limestone ½ to 1 foot thick that lies beneath the Herrin (No. 6) coal and is commonly separated from it by a thin shale or "fireclay" may be the St. David limestone, and if so, it is the only representative of the cyclothem that can be recognized in the quadrangle.

BRERETON CYCLOTHEM[21]

Much of the test drilling and all the core drilling in the Carlinville quadrangle have been undertaken to determine the position and thickness of the Herrin (No. 6) coal. The Brereton cyclothem is therefore represented in most of the records in the quadrangle.

It includes the Vermilionville[22] sandstone at its base, limestone, underclay, Herrin (No. 6) coal, black shale, limestone, and shale. In many records this cyclothem is represented not by a typical succession but by a considerable repetition of beds, which may be the result only of errors in the drillers' records or may actually reflect depositional conditions.[23]

---

[17]Wanless, H. R., *in* Illinois Geol. Survey Bull. 60, fig. 45, p. 190, 1931.
[18]Willman, H. B., and Payne, J. N., Illinois Geol. Survey Bull. 66, fig. 50, p. 106, 1942.
[19]Named for Pleasantview, Schuyler County, Ill. Wanless, H. R., Geology and mineral resources of the Alexis quadrangle: Illinois Geol. Survey Bull. 57, p. 90, 1929.

[20]Named for the town of St. David in Fulton County, Ill. Wanless, H. R., Geol. Soc. Amer. Spec. Paper 17, p. 102, 1939. Wanless, H. R., *in* Illinois Geol. Survey Bull. 60, p. 182, 1931.
[21]Named for the town of Brereton in Fulton County, Ill. Wanless, H. R., Geol. Soc. Amer. Spec. Paper 17, p. 78, 1939. Wanless, H. R., *in* Illinois Geol. Survey Bull. 60, p. 182, 1931.
[22]Named for the village of Vermilionville, LaSalle County, Ill. Cady, G. H., Illinois Geol. Survey Min. Inv. Bull. 10, p. 29, 1915.
[23]In north-central Illinois a variable number of shales, coals, and limestones occur below the Herrin (No. 6) coal; in the Carlinville quadrangle the variability occurs above the coal. Willman, H. B., and Payne, J. N., Illinois Geol. Survey Bull. 66, pp. 128-130, 1942.

With the exception of the basal sandstone (possibly not penetrated by the drill) the typical members of the cyclothem are recognized in the records of the A. W. Crawford No. 8 well and the Standard Oil Mine No. 2 shaft, both in sec. 29, T. 11 N., R. 6 W. (Nilwood Twp.), and of the Mudgett-Goebelt No. 8 well, SW ¼ sec. 20, T. 10 N., R. 7 W. (Carlinville Twp.).

The Herrin (No. 6) coal[24] is the distinguishing feature of the cyclothem. It is known in the southern and western parts of the state as the "blue band" coal. The "blue band" is a persistent clay parting, not uncommonly pyritic, occurring 1 to 2 feet above the base of the coal, and it has been reported in several of the records in the quadrangle. It probably underlies the entire quadrangle at depths ranging from 204 feet in the northwest part of the quadrangle to 319 feet in the vicinity of Coops Mound,[25] or at elevations respectively 478 and 293 feet above sea level. It ranges generally from 3 to 8 feet thick, but west of Girard a thickness of only 6 inches is reported (pl. 4).

The coal is bright banded bituminous coal composed mainly of clarain with between 10 and 20 percent of vitrain and still less fusain.

The Herrin limestone, the cap limestone of the Herrin (No. 6) coal, is recognized in the samples of some wells and in the records of most mine shafts in the quadrangle. It is reported in most of the records in which the coal bed is reported and is believed to occur throughout the quadrangle. It is the lower of two limestones in the Mudgett-Goebelt No. 8 well and in the Goodman-Reinecke Victor No. 1 well, SE ¼ sec. 17, the Standard Oil Company mine shaft B, NE ¼ sec. 21, and the South Mine shaft, SW ¼ sec. 33, T. 10 N., R. 7 W. (Carlinville Twp.).

The Herrin limestone is a gray, dense, hard limestone, in one instance pyrite-bearing, 4 to 12 feet thick.

Gray shale under the coal is reported in the Mudgett-Goebelt No. 8 well, and the limestone nodules reported in this shale may represent the lowermost limestone (Unit 3) of the cyclothem.

In this same well gray pyritic shale 4 feet thick occurs between the coal and the cap limestone, and in the Lagers-Bristow No. 1 well, NE ¼ sec. 7, T. 11 N., R. 7 W. (South Otter Twp.), there is 2 feet of tough black shale at this horizon.

The uppermost limestone (Unit 9) is 4 feet thick in the Mudgett-Goebelt No. 8 well, and it is also reported in the Goodman-Reinecke Victor well, in the Standard Oil Company mine shaft B, and in the South Mine near Carlinville. In the first well the shale (Unit 8) separating the uppermost limestone from the Herrin limestone is dark gray and 3 feet thick; in the last well it is only a few inches thick.

Shales of considerable thickness occur in the Brereton cyclothem above the Herrin limestone in the southeast part of the quadrangle. A gray silty, carbonaceous shale 38 feet thick rests directly on the Herrin (No. 6) coal in the Turner-Chamness No. 1 well, NE ¼ sec. 4, T. 9 N., R. 6 W. (Honey Point Twp.). In the Wilmington Star Coal Company's test boring in the SE ¼ sec. 32, T. 10 N., R. 6 W. (Shaw Point Twp.), the shale is 18 feet thick, "blue" except for 8 inches at the base which is black. Only a few miles northeast of the Turner-Chamness No. 1 well the shale is 32 feet thick.

McLEANSBORO GROUP[26]

As already stated, all the bedrock exposed in the Carlinville quadrangle belongs to the McLeansboro group of the Pennsylvanian system. However, the exposed bedrock strata are representative only of the Scottville and younger cyclothems (table 3); the older cyclothems are known only from the records, samples, and cores of wells and test borings. These are numerous, as all test borings go as deep as No. 6 coal

---

[24]Named for the town of Herrin in Williamson County, Ill., where the coal has been mined extensively. Shaw, E. W., and Savage, T. E., U. S. Geol. Survey Atlas, Murphysboro-Herrin folio (No. 185), p. 14, 1912.

[25]R. W. Hunt Company test drilling D-9, SW ¼ sec. 17, T. 10 N., R. 6 W. (Shaw Point Twp.).

[26]Named for the town of McLeansboro, Hamilton County, Ill., near which a diamond drill boring provided a good record of the upper "Coal Measures." De Wolf, F. W., Studies of Illinois coal, Introduction: Illinois Geol. Survey Bull. 16, p. 181, 1910.

TABLE 3.—SUCCESSION AND CLASSIFICATION OF THE McLEANSBORO GROUP EXPOSED IN THE CARLINVILLE QUADRANGLE[a]

		Thickness Ft.	In.
McWain sandstone			
76	Sandstone, massive, micaceous, light gray; interbedded gray shales at base; contains a few discontinuous lenses of coal	9	
Shoal Creek cyclothem			
75	Limestone, dense, light gray, poorly bedded, nodular, abundantly fossiliferous	7	
74	Limestone, more massive in upper part than in lower part, green gray; grades into overlying limestone	1	6
73	Shale, clayey, calcareous, soft, gray, fossiliferous	1	1
72	Shale, bituminous, locally calcareous, subcuboidal jointing; contains worm borings	1	6
71	Shale, somewhat calcareous, black, hard; contains conodonts, fish scales and spines, and occasional flakes of gypsum	2	3
70	Shale, calcareous, black, hard, poorly bedded, fossiliferous		5–6
69	Shale, calcareous, brownish gray, fossiliferous		½
68	Shale, clayey, calcareous, dark gray, sparsely fossiliferous; limestone concretions, up to 4 inches in thickness and 12 inches across and containing pyritized fossils, near the top	2	2
67	Shale, clayey, noncalcareous, light gray, "iron" stained		2½
66	Clay, noncalcareous, poorly bedded, light to medium bluish gray, some suggestion of lamination		8½
65	Clay, harder than the above, slightly calcareous, medium gray		7
64	Limestone, shaly, medium gray, fossiliferous		¼
63	Shale, slightly calcareous, gray		2
62	Limestone, very fossiliferous		½
61	Shale, slightly calcareous, medium gray; contains marine fossils and traces of wood		9
60	Limestone, bluish gray, highly fossiliferous; contains *Murchisonia* or *Worthenia* (?)		1½–2
59	Shale, bluish gray, thin-bedded, fossiliferous; contains *Leda* and carbonaceous woody material		4
58	Limestone, medium to dark bluish gray; contains *Aviculopecten, Murchisonia, Bellerophon*		½–1

[a]This table is compiled from the descriptions of the strata at certain localities (items 1-12 in sec. 10, T. 11 N., R. 8 W., geologic sections 1 and 3; items 13-21 in sec. 30, T. 10 N., R. 7 W., geologic section 10; items 22-75 in sec. 2, T. 9 N., R. 7 W., and sec. 35, T. 10 N., R. 7 W., geologic section 19; and item 76 in sec. 25, T. 10 N., R. 7 W., geologic section 29) and consequently is strictly applicable only at those localities. However, it does represent the general succession, and with due allowance for local variations in the lithology and the thicknesses of the strata, it is generally applicable in the entire quadrangle and a considerable area around the quadrangle.

		Thickness Ft.	In.
57	Shale, light blue gray, thin-bedded		5
56	Limestone, medium to dark bluish gray, subcrystalline, moderately fossiliferous, with *Aviculopectens* and gastropods		1½
55	Shale, bluish gray, thin-bedded		1–1½
54	Limestone, dark bluish gray, fossiliferous		1½
53	Shale, bluish gray		1½
52	Limestone		¼–1½
51	Shale, medium gray		5½
50	Shale, highly calcareous, dark gray to black, soft, fossiliferous; contains *Aviculopecten, Leda*, etc.	1	10
49	Limestone; contains numerous thin-shelled pelecypods		½
48	Coal, bright, irregular discontinuous band		¼
47	Clay, brownish gray; joints filled with secondary calcite		7
46	Clay, calcareous, dark gray		3
45	Clay, light gray streaked with brown grading to medium gray; contains small rounded or uneven limestone nodules	1	10
44	Clay, calcareous, light greenish gray; contains nodules up to 2 inches in diameter; grades into the overlying shale	1	6
43	Shale, calcareous, greenish gray, poorly laminated above, becoming well and thinly bedded below, with limestone concretions up to 6 or 8 inches in maximum diameter	1	10
42	Shale, calcareous, sandy, almost a sandstone or siltstone, greenish gray		3–4
Macoupin cyclothem			
41	Limestone, dense, reddish, nodular, poorly bedded, fossiliferous		8
40	Shale, calcareous, light bluish gray, well bedded; contains flattened oval greenish-gray limestone concretions up to 1½ inches thick near top		1
39	Shale, calcareous, micaceous, with lens-like masses of calcareous sandstone, greenish gray, slightly fossiliferous and containing peculiar trail markings		1
38	Limestone, blue gray when fresh, weathers to streaky rusty brown, densely crystalline, fossiliferous, nodular		5
37	Shale, calcareous, micaceous, greenish gray, with scattered discoidal clay-ironstone concretions displacing the shale laminae by their growth; joints filled with calcite and limonite		4
36	Limestone, crinoidal, granular, greenish, brownish, and dark gray; abundantly fossiliferous, with *Spirifer cameratus*		8
35	Shale, calcareous, fossiliferous, greenish gray, lower part dark gray, with flattened oval nodules of crystalline limestone		6–8

No.	Description	Ft.	In.
34	Shale, slightly calcareous, dark gray, fairly hard, unevenly bedded; contains some brownish limestone concretions in lower part	1	
33	Shale, black, hard, laminated; contains conodonts	1	1½
32	Clay, calcareous, dark gray, soft, fossiliferous; contains *Productids*		1½
31	Coal, bright bands, dull on bony lamination planes, thin-bedded		8
30	Underclay, noncalcareous		½
29	Underclay, greenish gray; small calcareous concretions near base		9
28	Underclay, calcareous, bluish to greenish gray, starchy fracture; varies from nongritty to sandy; contains calcareous nodules up to ¼ inch in diameter and very small crystals of marcasite	6	
27	Shale, calcareous, slightly silty, bluish or greenish gray, thin-bedded, platy; contains calcarous concretions	1	6
26	Sandstone and sandy shales, interbedded, micaceous, highly calcareous (the top 2 inches is especially calcareous), bluish gray, ripple-marked; thin- to medium-bedded; the thicker beds have peculiar markings	2–3	

Burroughs beds

No.	Description	Ft.	In.
25	Shale, somewhat micaceous, light greenish gray, thin-bedded; locally includes thin beds of siltstone, sandstone, and limestone	2	5
24	Limestone, sandy, bluish gray, crystalline, irregularly bedded, very fossiliferous, with occasional pebbles of limestone material	3	
23	Sandstone, noncalcareous, fine-grained, interlaminated with greenish shale		1–9

Carlinville cyclothem

No.	Description	Ft.	In.
22	Shale, slightly silty, noncalcareous, greenish gray; contains clay "ironstone" concretions	15	
21	Limestone, finely crystalline, dark gray, fossiliferous	4	7
20	Shale, calcareous, black, fairly hard, thin-bedded, slightly fossiliferous		1–6
19	Limestone, dense, dark gray		5
18	Shale, slightly calcareous, greenish gray; contains thin coaly flakes		3
17	Coal, bony to sublustrous		1
16	Shale, slightly calcareous, slightly gritty, dark gray, thin-bedded, with abundant leaf and stem impressions		6

No.	Description	Ft.	In.
15	Shale, micaceous, light to medium gray, soft, thin-bedded, with plant impressions and small calcareous concretions along bedding planes		9
14	Sandstone, micaceous, calcareous in the more massive beds, medium gray, fine-grained, friable; strata range from less than an inch to 6 inches in thickness; contains flakes of carbonaceous material	3	6
13	Sandstone, micaceous, medium bluish gray with streaks of yellow gray, flaky	6+	

Trivoli cyclothem

No.	Description	Ft.	In.
12	Shale, silty, noncalcareous, light yellow gray, evenly laminated, thin- to medium-bedded	7	6
11	Shale, noncalcareous, nongritty, light gray, evenly bedded, with a few light blue-gray slightly calcareous "ironstone" concretions containing fragments of *Calamites* and other plants	6	
10	Shale, noncalcareous or faintly calcareous, black, hard, fossiliferous		1½–2
9	Shale, thin-bedded; contains bony coal		¼
8	Coal (No. 8), hard, bright, somewhat bony		5–6
7	Underclay, dark gray, soft	2	
6	Underclay, medium to light gray, noncalcareous down to about 8 inches below coal	1	
5	Underclay, harder than the above, medium gray, slickensided; contains small calcareous concretions		9
4	Sandstone, calcareous, micaceous, platy, light yellow gray, spotted with brownish weathering stains, fine-grained; beds of variable thickness	1	
3	Sandstone, light yellow gray, mottled with brown patches where fresh, brown where weathered; evenly bedded in thin strata; some ripple marks	2	8

Scottville cyclothem

No.	Description	Ft.	In.
2	Shale, sandy, olive where fresh, weathering to grayish green, alternating with lenses of yellow micaceous sand; proportion of shale increases downward	3	9
1	Shale, slightly micaceous, light gray, relatively free from sand, decidedly soft, jointing not conspicuous; contains a few flattened concretions of clay "ironstone"	3	5

and thus pass completely through the Mc-Leansboro group. The greatest thickness of the group so far reported in the quadrangle is 326 feet in the Pittsburg-Buffalo No. 6 well in the SW ¼ SW ¼ SE ¼ sec. 33, T. 10 N., R. 6 W. (Shaw Point Twp.). The aggregate thickness of the exposed strata totals nearly 110 feet.

JAMESTOWN[27] AND BANKSTON FORK[28] CYCLOTHEMS

Strata apparently comprising representatives of either or both the Jamestown and Bankston Fork cyclothems are reported in the Carlinville quadrangle. These strata are best differentiated in the records of the Royal Colliery Company test boring, NW ¼ sec. 18, T. 12 N., R. 6 W. (Virden Twp.), of a test boring in the SE ¼ sec. 30, T. 12 N., R. 6 W. (Girard Twp.), of the shaft of the Virden Mine, SE ¼ sec. 9, T. 12 N., R. 6 W. (Virden Twp.), and of wells in the NE ¼ sec. 9, T. 11 N., R. 8 W. (North Palmyra Twp.) and in the NW ¼ sec. 6, T. 10 N., R. 6 W. (Shaw Point Twp.).

The thickness of the strata is never great, amounting to 27½ and 33 feet respectively in the first two instances cited above. It comprises underclay, coal, dark shale, gray shale, limestone, and shale.

The underclay is reported in a few records. It is 2 feet thick in the Virden mine shaft. The coal is present only in the last four records cited above. In the Virden mine shaft it is 1 foot 6 inches thick, and in the last two wells only 7 and 6 inches thick, respectively. In the Virden mine shaft the coal is 21 feet above the Herrin (No. 6) coal, and in the last two wells the interval between the two coals is 18 feet. In the second record cited the coal is separated from the overlying limestone by a foot of dark shale.

Limestone (Unit 7) is present in at least 30 of the drill records in the quadrangle. It ranges from 1½ to 6 feet in thickness,

and its average thickness is about 4½ feet. It is dense, compact, gray, and fossiliferous.

SPARLAND CYCLOTHEM[29]

The Sparland cyclothem, which includes coal No. 7 and the Piasa limestone, is most completely differentiated in the quadrangle in the record of the core of the Standard Oil Company's test boring in the NW ¼ sec. 9, T. 10 N., R. 6 W. (Shaw Point Twp.), as follows:

	Thickness in feet
Shale, fine-grained, gray............	4
Shale, dark greenish gray...........	3
Limestone, greenish gray, mottled...	⅓
Shale, greenish, fragmental.........	2⅔
Shale, greenish....................	1¼
Coal, good........................	2
Clay, greenish, shale...............	2⅙

Other representative sequences are described in the records of the Massa farm test boring No. 8 in the SE ¼ sec. 4 of the same township and of the A. W. Crawford No. 7 test boring in the SE ¼ sec. 30, T. 12 N., R. 6 W. (Girard Twp.). The basal sandstone is not reported in these records; where it or a basal sandy shale is present, the coal generally seems to be absent. The average thickness of the Sparland cyclothem in the quadrangle is about 21 feet.

Danville (No. 7) coal[30]

Coal that is believed to be the correlative of the Danville (No. 7) coal is reported in about 25 of the records of test holes or mine shafts in the quadrangle. It ranges from 3 inches to 2½ feet in thickness and is 23 to 34, usually less than 30, feet above the Herrin (No. 6) coal.

Piasa limestone[31]

The records of many of the test borings and wells in the quadrangle report the Piasa limestone. In 31 wells it ranges from 46 to 24 feet and lies at an average of 32 feet above the Herrin (No. 6) coal. Its average

[27]Named for Jamestown, Perry County, Ill.
[28]Contains the Bankston Fork limestone, which is named for Bankston Creek in southern Illinois. Cady, G. H., The areal geology of Saline County: Ill. Acad. Sci. Trans., vol. 19, p. 261, 1926. Bell, A. H., *et al.*, Geology of the Pinckneyville and Jamestown areas, Perry County, Illinois: Illinois Geol. Survey Ill. Petr. 19, fig. 2, p. 3, 1931.

[29]Named for the town of Sparland, Ill. Wanless, H. R., Illinois Geol. Survey Bull. 60, p. 182, 1931. Willman, H. B., and Payne, J. N., Illinois Geol. Survey Bull. 66, footnote 79, p. 136, 1942.
[30]Named for Danville, Ill. Bannister, H. M., Geology of Vermilion County: *in* Worthen, A. H., *et al.*, Geol. Survey of Illinois, vol. IV, pp. 250-251, 1870.
[31]Named for Piasa Creek, Jersey, Macoupin, and Madison counties, Ill. Culver, H. E., Coal resources of District III: Illinois Geol. Survey Coop. Min. Ser. Bull. 29, p. 20, 1925.

Fig. 7.—Upper shale of the Scottville cyclothem and basal sandstone of the Trivoli cyclothem, in the SW ¼ sec. 10, T. 11 N., R. 8 W. (South Palmyra Twp.) (geologic section 1). The protruding ledge is the basal stratum of the Trivoli cyclothem.

thickness is about 4 feet, but it has a maximum thickness of 6 feet. It is a crystalline, fragmental, fossiliferous, faintly laminated limestone mixed with some green clay or shale.

Shales above the Piasa limestone

In some borings the shales above the Piasa limestone are from 20 to 27 feet thick, which is as much or more than the average thickness of 21 feet of the entire cyclothem.

GIMLET CYCLOTHEM[32]

In outcrops in Macoupin County the strata that are believed to be the Gimlet cyclothem generally comprise, in ascending order, limestone, clay, coal, and shale.[33] The succession is very different from that in north-central Illinois, where the cyclothem rarely includes coal but does include the prominent Lonsdale limestone. In the Carlinville quadrangle, the cyclothem thickens, a basal sandstone or sandy shale is present, and the uppermost shale is thicker and sometimes contains bands of limestone, ironstone concretions, or dark or black "slate."

The coal ranges in thickness from 6 to 18 inches and lies 44 to 67 feet above the Herrin (No. 6) coal. The name Scottville was recently proposed for this coal,[34] but in order to avoid confusion that name should be applied to the coal that occurs in the next higher cyclothem which includes the Scottville limestone.

SCOTTVILLE CYCLOTHEM

The name Scottville is here proposed for the cyclothem which includes the Scottville limestone, not only because it includes that limestone but also because it is well exposed in the vicinity of Scottville. The type outcrop near the west limits of the village includes basal sandstone and shale, underclay, coal, fossiliferous shale, and the Scottville limestone. The limestone and higher strata of the cyclothem are exposed also north and east of Scottville.

The Scottville cyclothem is the oldest that crops out in the Carlinville quadrangle, the upper shale being exposed in the northwest part of the quadrangle (fig. 7).

[32]Named for Gimlet Creek, west of Sparland, Marshall County, Ill. Wanless, H. R., *in* Illinois Geol. Survey Bull. 60, pp. 179-193, 1931.

[33]Wanless, H. R., personal communication.

[34]Payne, J. N., Structure of Herrin (No. 6) coal in Macoupin County, etc.: Illinois Geol. Survey Circ. 88, p. 4, 1942.

The coal, 2 inches thick, lies about 4 feet below the Scottville limestone in the typical locality. What is believed to be the same coal has been reported in about ten of the records of borings in the Carlinville quadrangle, where it ranges from 64 to 89 feet above the top of the Herrin (No. 6) coal and from 4 inches to 3 feet in thickness. It is either absent in the other borings or has not been reported because it is too thin to be noted.

Scottville limestone[35]

The Scottville limestone is a dark gray limestone, dense to finely crystalline in texture, so fossiliferous that its fossil content is noted in some of the drilling records. In many of the drill records in the Carlinville quadrangle it is from 80 to 100 feet, or an average of about 88 feet, above the Herrin (No. 6) coal bed. It ranges from 1 foot to $6\frac{1}{2}$ feet in thickness, but its average thickness is a little more than $2\frac{1}{2}$ feet. It may possibly be correlated with the Exline limestone of Iowa and of western Illinois.[36]

Upper shale

More than 7 feet of the shale at the top of the Scottville cyclothem is exposed in the SW $\frac{1}{4}$ sec. 10, T. 11 N., R. 8 W. (South Palmyra Twp.) (geologic section 1[37] and fig. 7). The lower half of the exposed shale is light gray and not sandy, but the upper half is olive green and sandy with lenses of sandstone. There is a sharp contrast between the sandy shale and the overlying basal sandstone of the Trivoli cyclothem.

Bluish-gray nongritty noncalcareous clayey shale exposed in two outcrops along Massa Creek, respectively in the SE $\frac{1}{4}$ sec. 20 and in the SW $\frac{1}{4}$ sec. 21, T. 11 N., R. 8 W. (South Palmyra Twp.) (plate 1), is believed to belong also in the upper part of the Scottville cyclothem, as the outcrops are about 40 feet lower in elevation than the basal sandstone of the Trivoli cyclothem in

the outcrop in sec. 10 (geologic section 1), although the local structure (plate 4) is such that it may be in the Trivoli cyclothem. The shale is tenacious when wet, weathers yellowish brown, and in the outcrop in sec. 20 contains "ironstone" nodules.

TRIVOLI CYCLOTHEM[38]

The Trivoli cyclothem crops out also in a few localities in the northwest part of the Carlinville quadrangle (pl. 1). According to the records of borings, it has an average thickness of 58 feet in the quadrangle. The cyclothem consists, in ascending order, of sandstone, underclay, coal (No. 8), dark shale, and gray shale[39] (geologic sections 1-5) (fig. 8).

Basal sandstone

As exposed in sec. 10, T. 11 N., R. 8 W. (South Palmyra Twp.) (geologic section 1, fig. 7), the basal sandstone of the Trivoli cyclothem is an even bed, nearly 3 feet thick, light yellowish gray, strongly mottled with small and large patches of brown, compact, distinctly laminated, and strongly calcareous in the upper part. Occasionally some of the bedding planes show ripple marks, and mica flakes are mixed with the sand grains. The mottled appearance of the sandstone makes it a distinctive rock.

Traces of this or a similarly mottled sandstone occur in the SE $\frac{1}{4}$ NW $\frac{1}{4}$ sec. 10, T. 11 N., R. 8 W. (South Palmyra Twp.), and in the N $\frac{1}{2}$ sec. 26, T. 12 N., R. 8 W. (North Palmyra Twp.), where mottled calcareous sandstone crops out along the creek bottom and at the base of the valley walls. However, it is uncertain whether the sandstone at these localities is the basal member of the Trivoli or of the Carlinville cyclothem. A gray to yellowish-brown, fine-textured, slightly calcareous sandstone with marine fossils, especially of a brachiopod, probably *Derbya,* exposed in the east valley wall of Bear Creek, in the SE $\frac{1}{4}$ NE $\frac{1}{4}$ SW $\frac{1}{4}$ sec. 21, T. 10 N., R. 8 W. (Bird

[35]Named for the village of Scottville, Ill. Payne, J. N., *op. cit.,* p. 4.
[36]Weller, J. M., Wanless, H. R., Cline, L. M., and Stookey, D. G., Interbasin Pennsylvanian correlations, Illinois and Iowa: Bull. Amer. Assoc. Petr. Geol., vol. 28, n. 1692, 1942.
[37]The geologic sections are given in Appendix A.

[38]Named for the village of Trivoli, Peoria County, Ill. Wanless, H. R., Geol. Soc. Amer. Spec. Paper 17, p. 104, 1939; and *in* Illinois Geol. Survey Bull. 60, p. 182, 1931.
[39]The limestone (Unit 7 of the ideal cyclothem) apparently does not occur in the Carlinville quadrangle, although it is present in western Illinois where the cyclothem is typically developed. Wanless, H. R., Pennsylvanian section in western Illinois: Bull. Geol. Soc. Amer., vol. 42, p. 810, 1931.

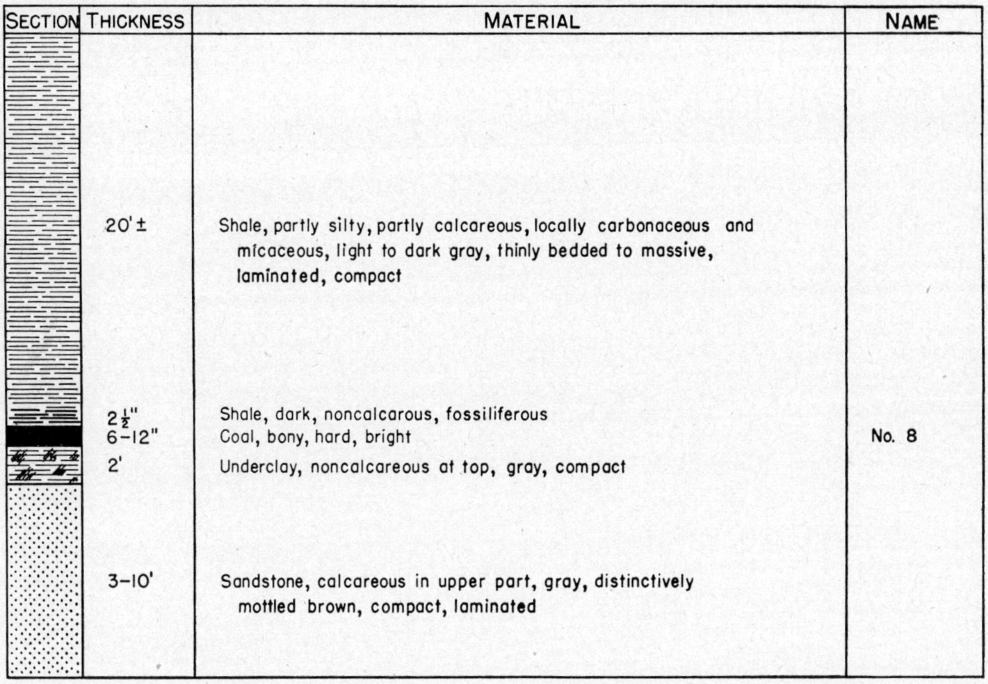

SECTION	THICKNESS	MATERIAL	NAME
	20'±	Shale, partly silty, partly calcareous, locally carbonaceous and micaceous, light to dark gray, thinly bedded to massive, laminated, compact	
	2½"	Shale, dark, noncalcarous, fossiliferous	
	6–12"	Coal, bony, hard, bright	No. 8
	2'	Underclay, noncalcareous at top, gray, compact	
	3–10'	Sandstone, calcareous in upper part, gray, distinctively mottled brown, compact, laminated	

FIG. 8.—Generalized section of outcrops of the Trivoli cyclothem in the Carlinville quadrangle.

Twp.), and a fossiliferous, very calcareous sandstone exposed at a nearby locality (geological section 2) and in the bed of the creek farther upstream, in the NW¼ SE ¼ sec. 21, same township, are believed to be also the basal member of the Trivoli cyclothem. They lie at an elevation about 20 feet lower than the basal sandstone in sec. 10, T. 11 N., R. 8 W. (South Palmyra Twp.) (geologic section 1, fig. 7).

Underclay

As exposed (geologic section 3) the underclay is nearly two feet thick, medium to dark gray, noncalcareous in the uppermost eight inches, below which it is permeated with small calcareous concretions. The lower part of the clay is more compact, with occasional slickensides or slip-fracture surfaces.

No. 8 coal

Where exposed in the Carlinville quadrangle (geologic sections 3 and 4), No. 8 coal has a maximum thickness of only 6 inches, but according to the records, 10 to 12 inches was encountered in some test borings. In other parts of the state it is as much as 2 feet thick. It is hard, bright, and bony.

Dark shale above the coal

As exposed in the Carlinville quadrangle (geologic section 3), the dark shale (Unit 6 of the ideal cyclothem) is not more than 2½ inches thick, is compact, practically noncalcareous, and mixed with bony coal, and, in the lower part, carries abundantly a species of *Lingula* and plant remains, mostly stem fragments, probably of *Calamites*. Locally, the bedding planes in the shale are covered with fine needles and rosettes of a mineral, possibly gypsum.

Gray shale

The uppermost shale in the cyclothem is nonsilty to silty, noncalcareous to slightly calcareous, locally carbonaceous and micaceous, ranges from light to dark bluish gray, weathers light yellow gray to brown, and is thinly bedded to massive, well laminated and locally platy, compact, and brittle. It

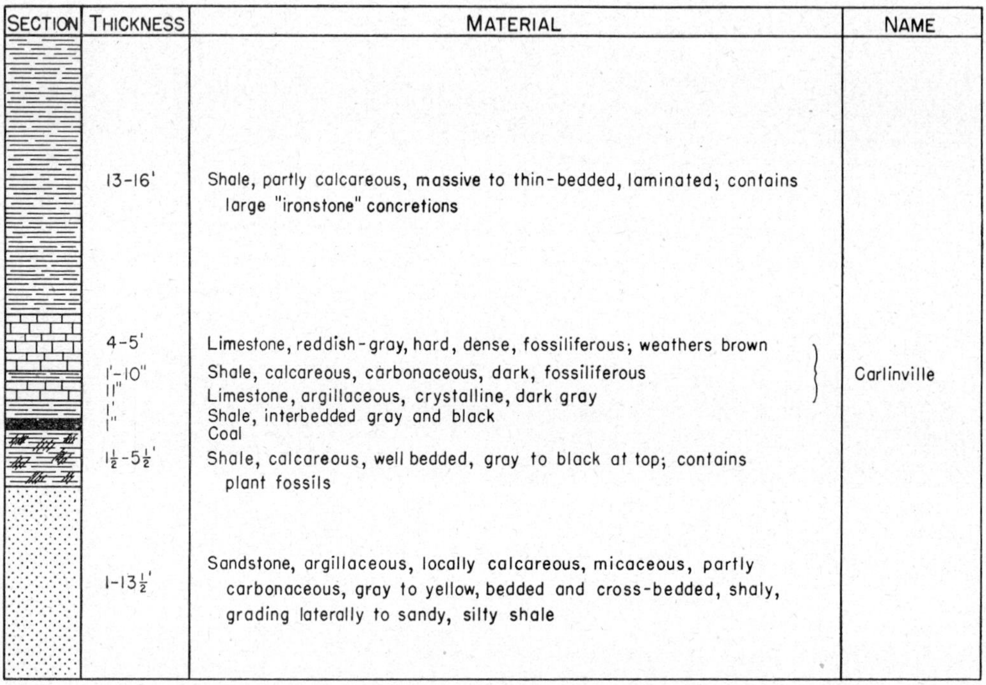

SECTION	THICKNESS	MATERIAL	NAME
	13-16'	Shale, partly calcareous, massive to thin-bedded, laminated; contains large "ironstone" concretions	
	4-5'	Limestone, reddish-gray, hard, dense, fossiliferous; weathers brown	
	1'-10"	Shale, calcareous, carbonaceous, dark, fossiliferous	Carlinville
	11"	Limestone, argillaceous, crystalline, dark gray	
	1'	Shale, interbedded gray and black	
	1"	Coal	
	1½-5½'	Shale, calcareous, well bedded, gray to black at top; contains plant fossils	
	1-13½'	Sandstone, argillaceous, locally calcareous, micaceous, partly carbonaceous, gray to yellow, bedded and cross-bedded, shaly, grading laterally to sandy, silty shale	

Fig. 9.—Generalized section of outcrops of the Carlinville cyclothem in the Carlinville quadrangle.

has a maximum thickness of at least 12 feet (geologic section 4). It is locally broken by joints about 6 to 7 inches apart. *Aviculopecten* and fossil fern leaves appear abundantly in the lower part of the shale, which also bears a few light blue-gray slightly calcareous "ironstone" concretions which contain fibrous plant fragments, possibly *Calamites*.

CARLINVILLE CYCLOTHEM[40]

The Carlinville cyclothem (fig. 9) is exposed in several localities in the quad-

[40]So named because it includes the Carlinville limestone. Wanless, H. R., Pennsylvanian section in western Illinois: Geol. Soc. Amer. Bull., vol. 42, pp. 801-812, 1931. The name Shoal Creek has also been' used for the cyclothem (Ekblaw, Sidney E., The question of the Shoal Creek and Carlinville limestones: Ill. Acad. Sci Trans., vol. 25, pp. 143-145, 1933) in the belief that the Carlinville limestone is the correlative of the Shoal Creek limestone in Clinton County (see p. 37); thus the cyclothem which includes it is the same as that which includes the Shoal Creek limestone. This latter usage was followed in Ball, John R., Some Pennsylvanian limestones of the Carlinville quadrangle, Illinois: Ill. Acad Sci. Trans., vol. 26, p. 97, 1934, and in Ball, John R., Pennsylvanian stratigraphy of the Carlinville, Illinois, quadrangle: Ill. Acad. Sci. Trans., vol. 36, pp. 147-150, 1943.
However, more recent studies (Simon, J. A., Correlation studies of Upper Pennsylvanian rocks in southwest-central Illinois: unpublished M. S. thesis, University of Illinois Department of Geology, 1946: Simon, J. A., and Cady, Gilbert H., Stratigraphic position of the Shoal Creek and Carlinville limestones in southwestern Illinois (abst.): Geol. Soc. Amer. Bull., vol. 57, p. 1231, 1946) have shown that the Carlinville limestone is not the correlative of the Shoal Creek limestone.

rangle, particularly in the vicinity of Carlinville and also in the northwestern part, near Palmyra (geologic sections 5-18). In many exposures only the limestone member of the cyclothem crops out. The maximum exposed thickness of the cyclothem in the Carlinville quadrangle is 37 feet (geologic section 7).

Sandstone

The basal sandstone of the Carlinville cyclothem (geologic sections 5-12) generally is somewhat argillaceous, micaceous, locally calcareous, occasionally carbonaceous, gray to yellow, and distinctly bedded. In some exposures it is cross-bedded, but in others only ripple marks or slightly wavy bedding are evident. Generally it includes more or less shale, sandy or silty and locally calcareous, and in the vicinity of Carlinville it consists mostly of shale (geologic sections 11 and 12).

Underclay and shale

The material underlying the coal or coal horizon is well exposed at many localities (geologic sections 6-12), generally in the

Fig. 10.—Shale and overlying Carlinville limestone along Macoupin Creek, N ½ sec. 3, T. 9 N., R. 7 W. (Brushy Mound Twp.).

same outcrops that show the basal sandstone. It is more shale than underclay and ranges from 1½ to 5½ feet in thickness.

It is well bedded, medium to dark gray, customarily black near the coal horizon, occasionally calcareous or with calcareous concretions, and frequently bears plant fossils. The plant fossils, including branches up to 1½ inches in thickness, in many instances are well enough preserved to be identified. A prominent feature is close-set jointing.

Coal

The coal or "bituminous shale" that underlies the Carlinville limestone has been designated the "No. 9 coal,"[41] but this designation is now applied to the coal of the Macoupin cyclothem (pp. 39-40). As exposed it is only about one inch thick (geologic sections 7 and 10).

Shale between coal and limestone

Neither the black laminated shale that commonly lies above the coal nor the calcareous marine shale which underlies the middle limestone and sometimes grades up-

ward into it is well represented in the Carlinville cyclothem in the Carlinville quadrangle. In one exposure (geologic section 8), interbedded light gray and black shales which contain not only plant remains and pyritic limestone concretions bearing *Chonetes* and crinoid stems but also some lenses and stringers of coal grade upward into a zone of soft gray shale or clay which is strongly calcareous and which immediately underlies the limestone. Unless the coal is present (geologic sections 6, 11-12), the shale above is not differentiated from the shale below the coal.

Carlinville limestone[42]

The Carlinville limestone is well exposed at a number of localities near Carlinville and in the vicinity of Palmyra. It crops out at several places along Macoupin Creek, in secs. 34 and 35, T. 10 N., R. 7 W. (Carlinville Twp.) and in secs. 3 and 4, T. 9 N., R. 7 W. (Brushy Mound Twp.) southeast of Carlinville (figs. 10-12); along Burroughs Branch, in sec. 33, T. 10 N., R. 7 W. (Carlinville Twp.), in and near the southeast part of Carlinville; along Hurricane Creek, in secs. 30 and 31, T. 10 N., R. 7 W.

[41]Worthen, A. H., Geology of Macoupin County: Geol. Survey of Illinois, vol. V, p. 287, 1873. (Log of mine shaft.)

[42]Named for Carlinville, Ill. Worthen, A. H., *op. cit.*, p. 290.

Fig. 11.—Carlinville limestone: an upper massive bed separated from a thinner lower one by dark shale. East of Terry Park in the NE ¼ sec. 34, T. 12 N., R. 8 W. (North Palmyra Twp.) (geologic section 8).

(Carlinville Twp.) west of Carlinville; and along Massa Creek and its tributaries in secs. 23, 26, 27, 34, and 35, T. 12 N., R. 8 W. (North Palmyra Twp.) (fig. 11) and in secs. 2, 3, and 10, T. 11 N., R. 8 W. (South Palmyra Twp.), northeast, east, and southeast of Palmyra (plate 1 and geologic sections. 6-15). Detached blocks of the Carlinville limestone are abundant on the gully slopes at several places in the northwest part of the quadrangle. They generally lie at about the same level, thus indicating that the parent ledge, concealed by soil and glacial drift, lies at about that level.

The Carlinville limestone member generally consists of two beds (fig. 11) of limestone separated by shale, the upper bed of limestone being much the thicker (geologic sections 8-10, 13). At some places there are three or four beds of limestone with intervening shale (geologic sections 6 and 7), and then two or three of the limestone beds with intervening shale are presumably the equivalent of one of the two beds usually observed. The average total thickness of the beds comprising the limestone member is about 4½ feet.

The upper limestone bed, usually massive although lamination is evident (fig. 12), is hard, dense, medium to dark gray or reddish when fresh but weathering light yellowish-brown to brown, and fossiliferous.

Fig. 12.—The upper member of the Carlinville limestone with joint faces deeply etched by solution, revealing the lamellar structure of the limestone, along Macoupin Creek in the NE ¼ sec. 3, T. 9 N., R. 7 W. (Brushy Mound Twp.).

The interbedded shale is calcareous, carbonaceous, and carboniferous, dark, well bedded, and compact, and ranges from 1 to 10 inches in thickness. It is fossiliferous and is marked in places by irregular lighter-colored tracings which may be worm trails.

The lower limestone bed is more argillaceous than the upper, and the bedding laminae are frequently irregular. It is dark gray when fresh, finely crystalline, and abundantly streaked with light and dark irregular markings that are suggestive of either some marine algal developments or possibly mollusc trails. It has a maximum thickness of 11 inches (geologic section 9).

The Carlinville limestone was originally tentatively correlated with the Shoal Creek limestone.[43] This correlation was maintained for some time,[44] but later the Carlinville limestone was believed to be somewhat lower and older than the Shoal Creek.[45] More recently the correlation of the two limestones as one and the same was reasserted,[46] and this usage was subsequently followed in some reports,[47] whereas in others they were still considered different.[48] The latest studies[49] have established that they are different.

[43]Worthen, A. H., Geology of Macoupin County: *in* Geology of Illinois, vol. V, p. 293, 1873.

[44]Udden, J. A., Notes on the Shoal Creek limestone: Illinois State Geol. Survey Bull. 8, Year-Book for 1907, pp. 118-126, 1907.

Weller, Stuart, The geological map of Illinois: Illinois State Geol. Survey Bull. 1, p. 21, 1906, and Bull. 6, p. 29, 1907.

[45]Lee, Wallace, Oil and gas in the Gillespie and Mt. Olive quadrangles, Illinois: Illinois Geol. Survey Bull. 31, pp. 82-84, 1915. (Excerpt published earlier.)

Kay, Fred H., Coal resources of District VII: Illinois Geol. Survey Coop. Min. Ser. Bull. IV, pp. 25-26, 1915.

Shaw, E. W., Description of the New Athens and Okawville quadrangles: U. S. Geol. Survey Atlas, folio No. 213, 1921.

Shaw, E. W., Description of the Carlyle and Centralia quadrangles: U. S. Geol. Survey Atlas, folio No. 216, 1923.

Lee, Wallace, Description of the Gillespie and Mt. Olive quadrangles: U. S. Geol. Survey Atlas, folio No. 220, 1926.

Wanless, H. R., Pennsylvanian section in western Illinois: Geol. Soc. Amer. Bull., vol. 42, pp. 801-812, 1931.

[46]Ekblaw, Sidney, The question of the Shoal Creek and Carlinville limestones: Ill. Acad. Sci. Trans., vol. 25, no. 4, pp. 143-145, 1932.

[47]Ball, J. R., Some Pennsylvanian limestones of the Carlinville quadrangle, Illinois: Ill. Acad. Sci. Trans., vol. 26, p. 97, 1934.

Wanless, H. R., Pennsylvanian correlations in the Eastern Interior and Appalachian coal fields: Geol. Soc. Amer. Spec. Paper 17, 1939.

Ball, J. R., Pennsylvanian stratigraphy of the Carlinville, Illinois, quadrangle: Ill. Acad. Sci. Trans., vol. 36, pp. 147-150, 1943.

[48]Payne, J. N., Structure of Herrin (No. 6) coal bed in Macoupin County, etc.: Illinois Geol. Survey Cir. 88, p. 5. 1942.

[49]Simon, J. A., *op. cit.;* and Simon, J. A., and Cady, Gilbert H., *op. cit.*

Shale overlying the Carlinville limestone

The upper shale of the Carlinville cyclothem is well exposed at only a few places in the Carlinville quadrangle. Most of the best exposures are in the vicinity of Carlinville (geologic sections 14, 15, 17, and 18), where the shale, although laminated, appears massive and nonbedded or thick-bedded, is noncalcareous or slightly calcareous, and contains large clay "ironstone" concretions, slightly calcareous. Other exposures (geologic sections 6, 7, 16) are near Palmyra, where the shale is thin-bedded and platy and the concretions are small.

The thickness of the shale at the one locality (geologic section 15) where both the overlying and underlying beds are present is nearly 16 feet; elsewhere as much as 14 or 15 feet is exposed (geologic sections 7 and 14). At one locality (geologic section 16) there are 33 feet of shale, but the presence of blocks of what is believed to be Carlinville limestone and its reported occurrence at about the same elevation in wells nearby[50] suggest that the lower 20 feet of this shale may lie below the limestone and only the upper 13 feet above the limestone. This would be in accord with the interval between the Carlinville limestone and the limestone member of the overlying Burroughs beds as recorded elsewhere in the quadrangle.

BURROUGHS BEDS

Between beds that are included respectively in the Carlinville and Macoupin cyclothems in the Carlinville quadrangle, there is exposed at numerous localities, especially near Carlinville, a succession of beds that do not seem to belong to either cyclothem. Neither do they comprise enough conventional units of a cyclothem to merit classification as such at this time. They are designated as *Burroughs beds* in this report, the name being derived from Burroughs Branch, the local name for the tributary of Macoupin Creek that flows southwest across the southeast corner of

[50]Rich, J. L., Manuscript map of geological structure of Carlinville quadrangle; in possession of W. E. Alderson and W. A. Wallace, Virden, Ill.

Carlinville and along which a typical exposure of the beds occurs (geologic section 17).

The succession appears to consist regularly of three members—a basal sandstone or sandy shale, a middle limestone, and a top shale (geologic sections 15-19). In many exposures only the limestone member is evident (geologic sections 21-24), and fragments of it frequently occur on hill slopes between gullies in which it is exposed. Stratigraphically, the limestone lies 14 to 17 feet above the Carlinville limestone, according to exposures and records of mine shafts and test borings in which both may be recognized.

The basal member is usually a gray fine-grained micaceous noncalcareous to calcareous sandstone commonly interlaminated with greenish shale and containing at its base a thin limestone bed. It locally exhibits mud cracks and ripple marks. It ranges usually between less than one and slightly more than one foot in thickness but may be as much as 4 feet thick (geologic section 16).

The middle limestone member is notably different from the Carlinville limestone below, but where weathered it resembles the Macoupin limestone above. Its fauna, however, is markedly different from that of the Macoupin and includes many specimens of the brachiopod genera *Productus* and *Dielasma*. It is commonly a fossiliferous crystalline gray sandy limestone, but it is occasionally dense or coarsely crystalline, and ranges through bluish gray or greenish gray to nearly black, weathering to yellowish, reddish, or purplish brown. It is irregularly bedded and nodular and may be shaly or even interlaminated with greenish shale. It ranges from a fraction of an inch to more than 5 feet in thickness.

The top shale is generally sandy, noncalcareous, micaceous, and light greenish gray, but locally it is calcareous (geologic sections 17 and 18) and usually ranges from 1 to 3 feet in thickness wherever it is present. At several localities it is seemingly absent (geologic sections 20-24). At one locality (geologic section 16), where it is at least 6 feet thick, in the north part of the quadrangle, the beds that have been correlated

as Burroughs beds, because they lie immediately above strata that are believed to be the uppermost shales of the Carlinville cyclothem, differ considerably from the typical Burroughs succession in that they consist mostly of noncalcareous sandstone and shale, with only one foot of calcareous sandstone near the middle, and are considerably thicker than the succession in the vicinity of Carlinville. It is possible that they are actually the lower beds of the Macoupin cyclothem, which they resemble closely, in which case the Burroughs beds were either never deposited in this locality or, as is more likely, if deposited they were eroded before the deposition of the Macoupin cyclothem. They are also somewhat similar to the McWain sandstone (pp. 44-45), although the upper beds are more shaly, and if they are correlated with the McWain sandstone, this is another example of the deep erosion that is believed to have preceded the McWain deposition.

The limestone member has been correlated with a sandy limestone that crops out near Centralia and has been included in what has been called the Centralia cyclothem.[51] Because there now exists some question not only about this correlation but also as to whether the beds that crop out in and near the Carlinville quadrangle may be only a somewhat unusual local development of beds either in the top of the Carlinville cyclothem, in the basal part of the Macoupin cyclothem, or in the transition from one to the other, the local name Burroughs has been used in order to avoid possible confusion if future studies reveal that the beds have regional stratigraphic significance.

MACOUPIN CYCLOTHEM

This cyclothem, which is named for Macoupin Creek, along which it is typically exposed, was distinguished and named during the early field work in the quadrangle, and its identity was recognized in subsequent publications.[52] Typical outcrops occur along Macoupin Creek and its tributaries on the east side of sec. 4, T. 9 N., R. 7 W.

[51]Ekblaw, Sidney E., *op. cit.*
[52]Wanless, H. R., Pennsylvanian section in western Illinois: Geol. Soc. Amer. Bull., vol. 42, pp. 801-812, 1931, and all later publications.

SECTION	THICKNESS	MATERIAL	NAME
	7-13'	Shale, silty or sandy, calcareous, micaceous, gray, thin-bedded, fossiliferous; contains "ironstone" concretions and lenses of fossiliferous limestone	
	1-5'	Limestone, gray, weathers red, crystalline, granular, generally well bedded, fossiliferous, locally shaly	Macoupin
	16-30"	Shale, locally calcareous, greenish-gray to black, soft to hard	
	0-13"	Limestone (local), crystalline, fossiliferous	
	10-15"	Shale, hard, lamininated, dark gray to black, fossiliferous	
	1-12"	Shale, partly calcareous, dark gray to black, hard to soft	
	3-9"	Coal, locally bony, soft, lustrous	No. 9 ?
	9"-3'	Underclay, noncalcareous to calcareous, soft to hard, gray	
	2-30"	Limestone, earthy, hard, dark gray to black, fossiliferous	
	1-7½'	Shale, calcareous, locally silty or sandy, gray, soft and clayey to hard and firm, thin-bedded to massive, locally coaly	
	0-8'	Sandstone or interbedded sandstone and shale, calcareous, micaceous, gray to brown, ripple-marked	

FIG. 13.—Generalized section of outcrops of the Macoupin cyclothem in the Carlinville quadrangle.

(Brushy Mound Twp.), upstream to the center of the east line of sec. 24, T. 10 N., R. 7 W. (Carlinville Twp.) (geologic sections 17, 19-34) (pl. 1). Its aggregate thickness in outcrops is slightly more than 20 feet (geologic sections 19 and 22), and it contains all the conventional members of a cyclothem (fig. 13). The Macoupin limestone in the type exposure (geologic section 19) is about 18 feet above the Burroughs limestone, but to the northeast they appear to converge (geologic sections 23 and 24), apparently because the upper shale member of the Burroughs beds and several strata in the lower part of the Macoupin cyclothem successively thin and terminate in that direction.

Basal sandstone

The basal member of the cyclothem is a sandstone or interbedded sandstone and shale, usually very calcareous, micaceous, bluish gray to brown, and ripple marked. It is usually 2-3 feet but may be as much as 8 feet thick (geologic section 17), and as already stated, it is absent to the northeast (geologic sections 21-24).

Lowermost shale

The lowermost shale member of the cyclothem is best exposed in the NW ¼ sec. 2, T. 9 N., R. 7 W. (Brushy Mound Twp.) (geologic section 19), where it attains its greatest thickness—7½ feet. It is a bluish-, greenish-, or brownish-gray fossiliferous calcareous locally silty or sandy shale, with calcareous nodules and concretions up to 5 inches in size. At some places it is soft and clayey, elsewhere it is hard and firm, thin-bedded and platy to massive. Locally it is coaly and includes a 1-inch seam of poor quality coal (geologic sections 23, 24, and 29). Where all of it is exposed, its thickness ranges from 1 to 7½ feet, increasing from northeast to southwest.

Lowermost limestone

The lowermost limestone of the Macoupin cyclothem appears to be present along Macoupin Creek only to the northeast (geologic sections 23, 24, 29-31). It is hard, fine-grained, dark gray to black, earthy or shaly, thin-bedded or laminated, and slabby or platy. It usually contains an abundance of both plant and invertebrate fossils, most of the latter being small high-spired gastropods. The limestone is usually 2 to 3 inches thick, but at one place (geologic section 23) it varies from 10 to 30 inches.

Underclay

The underclay is generally noncalcareous in the upper part and grades to calcareous in the lower part, which appears to be a transition zone to the lowermost limestone or to the underlying shale where the limestone is absent. The underclay locally contains calcareous nodules, especially in the lower part. It is generally nongritty, but locally it is silty or sandy. It ranges from light or dark gray, through purplish gray, light or dark bluish gray, greenish gray, olive gray, and yellowish gray to brown. It is usually soft and structureless, with some "slip" fractures, especially in the upper part, but locally it is crumbly, starchy, and fairly hard, and at some places it grades into thin-bedded, indistinctly bedded, or massive shale. It is commonly carbonaceous or coaly and locally contains one or two discontinuous seams of bony coal ¼ to ¾ of an inch thick (geologic sections 23, 24, and 29). It is usually 15-16 inches and ranges from 9 inches to 3 feet in thickness.

Coal No. 9

The coal of the Macoupin cyclothem, ranging from 3 to 9 inches in thickness, occurs regularly in the Carlinville quadrangle except where it has been eroded since Pennsylvanian time. It is lustrous, soft, and of inferior quality. In some places, it is so impure that it is "bony." When weathered it breaks into small, cubical fragments averaging about half an inch in diameter. It has sometimes been called the No. 9 coal, but it is not certain that this designation is correct as coals in other cyclothems have also been so designated (see page 35).

Strata between coal and middle (Macoupin) limestone

In the type outcrop (geologic section 19) and in other outcrops at nearby localities in sec. 2, T. 9 N., R. 7 W. (Brushy Mound Twp.) and secs. 35 and 26, T. 10 N., R. 7 W. (Carlinville Twp.) (geologic sections 25-28), the strata between the coal and the middle (Macoupin) limestone consist generally of a succession of three kinds of shale or clay. The bottom unit varies from a hard massive flaky nonfossiliferous greenish-yellow to dark gray or black noncalcareous shale to a soft crumbly fossiliferous dark gray carbonaceous calcareous clay and ranges from 1 to 12 inches thick. The middle unit is a hard laminated sheety fossiliferous dark gray to black noncalcareous shale 10 to 15 inches thick. The top unit is a soft to fairly hard thinly and unevenly bedded massive to flaky fossiliferous greenish-gray to dark gray to black noncalcareous or calcareous shale 16 to 30 inches thick. At one locality (geologic section 27) a bed of fossiliferous crystalline bluish-gray limestone 13 inches thick with overlying massive slip-fractured dark gray to black shale 7 inches thick occurs between the middle and the bottom shales. The total thickness of the strata in the sequence ranges from 3 to nearly 5 feet.

Farther northeast along Macoupin Valley, in secs. 24 and 25, T. 10 N., R. 7 W. (Carlinville Twp.) (geologic sections 23-24, 29-31), the interval between the coal and the middle limestone of the cyclothem is reduced to not more than 15 inches, and at some places (geologic sections 29 and 30) the limestone lies directly on the coal. The material representing the unit is fossiliferous yellowish-gray, bluish-gray, or dark gray calcareous clay or shale, which may be the same as the top shale of the type succession.

Macoupin limestone

The name Macoupin is restrictively applied to this limestone bed and not to any of the other limestone beds locally both lower and higher in the cyclothem, because it is the most consistently developed. It is 1 to 5 feet thick, bluish gray to greenish gray, weathering to a brick-red hue, crystalline, medium to coarsely granular, crinoidal, generally well-bedded and slabby but at some places poorly bedded or nodular, usually very fossiliferous, and locally carbonaceous. Also locally it includes occasional pockets or beds of greenish-gray shaly clay as much as 3 inches thick.

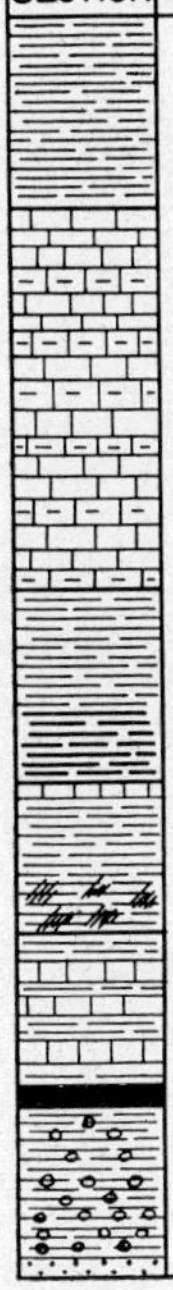

SECTION	THICKNESS	MATERIAL	NAME
	5'	Shale, calcareous, locally sandy and micaceous, bluish-gray	
	6-12'	Limestone, gray, weathers yellow, buff, pink, reddish-brown, crystalline, poorly bedded, flaggy, with shale partings, fossiliferous; lower part greenish-gray, more argillaceous and shaly than upper part	Shoal Creek
	$2\frac{1}{2}$-$3\frac{1}{2}$'	Shale, usually calcareous, gray, soft, thinly bedded, fossiliferous; contains concretions	
	4"-3'3"	Shale, calcareous, black, hard, laminated, very fossiliferous	
	0-2'8"	Shale, calcareous, dark gray, soft, fossiliferous; at top is concretionary band of limestone, dark, bluish-gray, hard, dense, very fossiliferous	
	0-1'9"	Shale or clay, noncalcareous, gray	
	0-5'	Shale, calcareous, bluish-gray, fossiliferous; contains bands of limestone, gray, dense, very fossiliferous	
	$\frac{1}{4}$"	Coal, bright; discontinuous band	
	6'4"	Shale, calcareous, dark gray to greenish-gray, locally sandy at base and noncalcareous at top; contains abundant calcareous nodules	

FIG. 14.—Generalized section of outcrops of the Shoal Creek cyclothem in the Carlinville quadrangle.

Uppermost shale

Where its entire thickness is exposed (geologic sections 19, 25, and 29), the marine shale above the Macoupin limestone ranges from slightly more than 7 to more than 13 feet in thickness. It is usually silty or slightly sandy, calcareous, micaceous, greenish or bluish gray, thinly bedded, and fossiliferous. It contains discoidal "ironstone" or calcareous concretions and concretionary bands and nodular beds of fossiliferous dense or finely crystalline bluish-gray limestone that weathers reddish-brown. These beds may be as much as 15 inches thick (geologic sections 19, 22, 25, and 32). Some of these limestone beds are reported in the records of some of the test borings in the quadrangle.

SHOAL CREEK CYCLOTHEM[53]

The Shoal Creek cyclothem in and around the Carlinville quadrangle has previously been called the LaSalle, with[54] and without interrogation,[55] and the Livingston,[56] in the belief that its thick limestone member was the correlative of the limestone member of those cyclothems. The establishment of the correlation of the limestone with the Shoal Creek limestone in Clinton County[57] simultaneously identified the cyclothem.

The best exposures of this cyclothem are in the SE ¼ NE ¼ sec. 26 (geologic section 22), the SE ¼ SE ¼ NE ¼ sec. 35 (geologic section 32), the SW ¼ SE ¼ sec. 35 (geologic section 19), and the center of the NW ¼ sec. 36, T. 10 N., R. 7 W. (Carlinville Twp.) (geologic section 35, fig. 22). The maximum thickness of the complete cyclothem as it is exposed at any one locality is 29 feet (geologic section 19), but inasmuch as the top member of the cyclothem at this locality is limestone, above which there are believed to be shale beds as exposed at several localities in T. 10 N., R. 6 W.

[53]So named because it includes the Shoal Creek limestone, which is named for Shoal Creek, along which it is typically exposed. Engelmann, Henry, Geology of Clinton County, *in* Geol. Survey of Illinois, vol. 3, p. 175, 1868.

[54]Ekblaw, Sidney E., The question of the Shoal Creek and Carlinville limestones: Ill. Acad. Sci. Trans., vol. 25, pp. 143-145, 1932.

[55]Ball, J. R., Some Pennsylvanian limestones of the Carlinville quadrangle, Illinois: Ill. Acad. Sci Trans., vol. 26, p. 97, 1934.
Wanless, H. R., Pennsylvanian correlations in the Eastern Interior and Appalachian coal fields: Geol. Soc. Amer. Spec. Paper 17, 1939.

[56]Ball, J. R., Pennsylvanian stratigraphy of the Carlinville, Illinois, quadrangle: Ill. Acad. Sci. Trans., vol. 36, pp. 147-150, 1943.

[57]Simon, J. A., *op. cit.*; and Simon, J. A., and Cady, Gilbert H., *op. cit.*

(Shaw Point Twp.) (page 44), the maximum aggregate thickness is probably somewhat greater.

The strata included in the cyclothem in this report may actually comprise two cyclothems, as there are two coal and noncalcareous clay or shale (underclay?) successions separated by a considerable thickness of fossiliferous calcareous shale and limestone beds. The lower cyclothem would comprise this calcareous shale-limestone succession, the lower coal-clay succession, and the underlying calcareous shale (beds 42-65, table 3; beds 20-43, geologic section 19; beds 4-8, geologic section 22; beds 3-9, geologic section 32; beds 1-3, geologic section 35; beds 1-3, geologic section 36; and bed 19, geologic section 25). Its existence has been tentatively recognized,[58] but it is not distinguished in this report because the local evidence is not conclusive.

For convenience of description in this report, the strata constituting the Shoal Creek cyclothem as herein defined are considered, from base upwards, to be (1) strata below lower coal horizon, (2) lower coal horizon, (3) calcareous marine shales between coal horizons, (4) noncalcareous clay and shale below upper coal horizon, (5) upper coal horizon, (6) calcareous marine shale and limestone between coal horizon and black shale, (7) black shale, (8) shale between black shale and Shoal Creek limestone, (9) Shoal Creek limestone, and (10) shale above Shoal Creek limestone. The first three of these units constitute what might be a cyclothem below and apart from the Shoal Creek cyclothem.

Unit 1. — *Strata below lower coal horizon*

The strata below the lower coal horizon of the Shoal Creek cyclothem as herein defined consist principally of light to dark gray or greenish-gray calcareous clay and shale. They contain abundant calcareous nodules which decrease in size upwards through the succession (beds 20-25, geologic section 19). At one locality (geologic section 19) the lower 3 to 4 inches is very sandy, and this is the only place where anything suggesting a basal sandstone was observed, unless the

[58]Wanless, *op. cit.*, 1931, figs. 2 and 7 and p. 812.

McWain sandstone (pp. 44-45) should prove to be this member. At this locality also the upper 7 inches of the unit is noncalcareous and suggests the weathered (?) zone or underclay that is normally expected below a coal.

Unit 2. — *Lower coal horizon*

The lower coal horizon is exposed at only one locality (geologic section 19) where it consists of a discontinuous band of bright coal not more than $1/4$ of an inch thick. At other localities where this horizon might have been exposed, it was covered by slump talus, so that its presence or absence could not be established.

Unit 3. — *Calcareous shale between coal horizons*

Between the two coal horizons there is as much as 5 feet of fossiliferous bluish-gray calcareous shale which contains nodules and bands of very fossiliferous dense gray limestone. The number of limestone bands varies, 8 occurring at one locality (geologic section 19), and they are as much as 3 inches thick.

Unit 4. — *Noncalcareous clay and shale below upper coal horizon*

At some localities (geologic sections 19, 22, and 36) there is gray noncalcareous clay or shale as much as $1\frac{3}{4}$ feet thick, which is believed to represent an underclay horizon. At other localities (geologic sections 32 and 35) the horizon is apparently absent. It would be locally the basal bed of the Shoal Creek cyclothem if the lower beds were distinguished as a separate cyclothem.

Unit 5. — *Upper coal horizon*

Noncalcareous or otherwise somewhat altered clay and shale below this horizon and black usually hard and laminated shale above it, with calcareous shale and limestone beds locally intervening, indicate that this is the normal position of coal in the conventional cyclothem. However, no coal was observed at this horizon in exposures in the Carlinville quadrangle, unless the coaly inclusions in bed 4, geologic section 35, may be so considered.

Unit 6. — Shale between upper coal horizon and black shale

Above the upper coal horizon there is usually (geologic sections 19, 22, and 32) a soft fossiliferous dark gray calcareous shale as much as 2 feet 8 inches thick. It includes, generally at the top, a conspicuous concretionary band of hard dense dark very fossiliferous bluish-gray limestone 4 to 5 inches thick. At one locality (geologic section 19) the top of the shale is a thin band of crushed shells.

Unit 7. — Black shale

This member of the Shoal Creek cyclothem is conspicuous in all outcrops showing this portion of the cyclothem (geologic sections 19, 22, 32, 35, 36). It is usually somewhat calcareous, black, hard, more or less well bedded or laminated, and very fossiliferous with pelecypods, fish spines and scales, and conodonts. It ranges in thickness from 4 inches to 3 feet 3 inches.

Unit 8. — Shale between black shale and Shoal Creek limestone

Above the laminated black shale is a clayey shale or clay that is usually calcareous, fossiliferous, gray or dark gray, soft, thinly bedded, and includes bands of concretions, but locally it is noncalcareous, nonfossiliferous, yellowish or greenish gray, and flaky (geologic sections 19, 22, and 35). It averages about 3 feet in thickness, ranging from 2 feet 7 inches to 3 feet 5 inches. It appears to grade into the overlying Shoal Creek limestone, as the upper part is more calcareous than the lower part and the lower part of the limestone is more argillaceous and includes beds of soft greenish- or yellowish-gray calcareous clay (geologic sections 22, 35, and 36). The absence of the shale in sec. 16, T. 11 N., R. 7 W. (South Otter Twp.) (geologic section 36), may be due to the fact that even the lower part of it has graded laterally into the limestone that lies immediately above at that locality. At some localities it also appears to grade downward into the black shale (geologic section 19).

Unit 9. — Shoal Creek limestone

The Shoal Creek limestone, previously designated by other names (see page 41, footnotes 53, 54, 55, 56, 57), is well exposed at numerous localities along Macoupin Creek and its tributaries from the south side of sec. 36, T. 10 N., R. 7 W. (Carlinville Twp.) (fig. 22), to the center of sec. 16, T. 10 N., R. 6 W. (Shaw Point Twp.) (pl. 1). Where it is not actually exposed, its presence in the valley slopes is frequently indicated by its nodular fragments on the surface of the slopes. It occurs high in the valley walls in the southwest part of its outcrop area and at successively lower positions to the northeast until in the northeasternmost outcrop it is at stream level. What is believed to be the Shoal Creek limestone also crops out in secs. 9, 10, and 16, T. 11 N., R. 7 W. (South Otter Twp.) (fig. 15), and it is reported in the records of many test borings in the east part of the Carlinville quadrangle.

The Shoal Creek limestone is usually gray or light gray, weathering to yellow, buff, pink, or reddish brown, is dense or finely crystalline, nodular, poorly bedded, and flaggy with soft, fossiliferous, greenish gray, calcareous, shaly partings, and is moderately to abundantly fossiliferous with the brachiopod genera *Composita* and *Marginifera* most abundant and one or more species of the cup coral *Lophophyllum* characteristic (Appendix C). The lower part of the limestone is generally greenish gray, is more argillaceous or earthy, contains more and thicker shaly partings than the upper part, and thus appears to grade vertically and in some cases laterally from the underlying shale.

Where exposed the limestone ranges from 6 feet to 9 feet 9 inches in thickness, but it is probable that this does not represent the maximum thickness. Thicknesses up to 12 feet have been reported in the records of test borings.

Unit 10. — Shale above the Shoal Creek limestone

Shale exposed in small areas in the stream bed, or for as much as 5 feet in the banks above the stream, of Sugar Creek in the

FIG. 15.—Shoal Creek limestone cropping out in stream valley in the NE ¼ sec. 16, T. 11 N., R. 7 W. (South Otter Twp.) (geologic section 36).

vicinity of Oakland School, SW ¼ sec. 31, T. 10 N., R. 6 W. (Shaw Point Twp.), SE ¼ sec. 36, T. 10 N., R. 7 W. (Carlinville Twp.), and NW ¼ sec. 6, T. 9 N., R. 6 W. (Honey Point Twp.), and farther downstream in secs. 29 and 30, and along the east side of Macoupin Creek in the NE ¼ sec. 20 and the NW ¼ sec. 21, T. 10 N., R. 6 W. (Shaw Point Twp.) is believed to be the top unit of the Shoal Creek cyclothem.

Generally the shale is calcareous, non-gritty, and bluish gray weathering to brown; occasionally it is sandy and micaceous. Concretions are not common, but in one outcrop in the SW ¼ sec. 31, T. 10 N., R. 6 W. (Shaw Point Twp.), there are calcareous concretions.

Shale overlying the Shoal Creek limestone in the NW ¼ sec. 27, T. 10 N., R. 6 W. (Shaw Point Twp.), differs considerably from that in the other outcrops in that it is well indurated, highly calcareous, sandy, and micaceous, greenish gray, carries abundant carbonaceous material on the bedding planes, and breaks in large irregular plates nearly an inch in thickness. This shale may be the basal bed of the cyclothem next above the Shoal Creek, or it may be a part of the McWain sandstone if the latter proves to be still younger in age.

McWain sandstone

The McWain sandstone is so called because it crops out frequently on one or the other of the several McWain farms in secs. 24 and 25, T. 10 N., R. 7 W. (Carlinville Twp.) (geologic sections 29, 33, and 34). The sandstone is somewhat massive and friable, varies from fine to coarse in texture, and is gray. In some exposures it is in beds that range from 1 to 8 inches in thickness. It is commonly micaceous, with large mica flakes, has carbonaceous lenses or coaly seams, and shows carbonaceous patches on bedding planes. It is locally cross-bedded and contains calcareous "ironstone" concretions. Near its uneven base are one or two interbedded shale lenses.

As this sandstone rests on the upper strata of the Macoupin cyclothem, it occupies the normal position of, and would therefore be generally considered, the basal sandstone of the Shoal Creek cyclothem. However, similar material has not been observed elsewhere in the base of the Shoal Creek cyclothem in the quadrangle; for this reason, and also because a similar massive sandstone lying on the Scottville limestone west of the quadrangle and on the Macoupin limestone north of the quadrangle has been interpreted as a younger deposit filling channels cut in the older beds,[59] it is thought that the Mc-Wain sandstone is probably a local example of this same channel sandstone. It is not known to occur at any other locality in the quadrangle unless the sandstone and shale in sec. 25, T. 12 N., R. 8 W. (see page 38), and the sandy shale in sec. 27, T. 10 N., R. 6 W. (see page 44), are representatives of it. Sandstone beds believed to be of the same age are reported in some test borings in the quadrangle.

POSSIBLE POST-PENNSYLVANIAN, PRE-PLEISTOCENE DEPOSITS

At two places along Macoupin Creek, one in the east bank in the SE ¼ sec. 26, T. 10 N., R. 7 W. (Carlinville Twp.), and the other in the west bank in the NE ¼ sec . 19, T. 10 N., R. 6 W. (Shaw Point Twp.), about a quarter of a mile below the Chicago and North Western Railway bridge, there are deposits of gravel that may be of some post-Pennsylvanian, pre-Pleistocene age. They lie on Pennsylvanian bedrock and at the base of the stream alluvium with which they are somewhat mixed. These gravels contain a large proportion of chert, quartzite, jasper, and quartz pebbles, all seemingly coated and more or less polished and glossy or "bronzed." This type of pebble is characteristic of deposits known elsewhere in Illinois and adjacent states and known to be of post-Pennsylvanian, pre-Pleistocene age. However, in the deposits in the Carlinville quadrangle they have been reworked to some extent as they are mixed with noncoated pebbles ordinarily found in Recent deposits, and so their occurrence can be interpreted only as indicating the presence of deposits of this age in or near the quadrangle.

---

[59]Wanless, H. R., Pennsylvanian section in western Illinois: Geol. Soc. Amer. Bull., vol. 42, p. 812, 1931.

CHAPTER V — PLEISTOCENE[1] STRATIGRAPHY

Glacial drift is "a mixture of clay, sand, gravel and boulders formed by glacial agencies,"[2] these agencies being the glacial ice itself and running water derived from it. The material deposited directly from the glacier, classified as *till,* consists principally of clay derived from the rocks over which the glaciers moved, not by chemical alteration of the rocks but by the intense grinding

above which generally groundwater escapes in the form of seepage or springs, (2) deposits of peat, and (3) associated silts containing molluscan fossils of Yarmouth age (Appendix C), or because the upper part of the older till, lying beneath calcareous Illinoian till, is leached and otherwise altered as a result of weathering during the intervening interglacial stage.

TABLE 4.—CLASSIFICATION OF THE PLEISTOCENE SYSTEM[a]

Rock terms: System Time terms: Period	Series Epochs	Stages Ages	Substages	Stages in Europe
Pleistocene or Glacial	Eldoran	Recent		
		Wisconsin (glacial)	Mankato (Lake Wisconsin) Cary (Middle Wisconsin) Tazewell (Early Wisconsin) Iowan	Würm
	Centralian	Sangamon (interglacial)		Riss-Würm
		Illinoian (glacial)		Riss
	Ottumwan	Yarmouth (interglacial)		Mindel-Riss
		Kansan (glacial)		Mindel
	Grandian	Aftonian (interglacial)		Günz-Mindel
		Nebraskan (glacial)		Günz

[a]Kay, G. F., and Leighton, M. M., Eldoran epoch of the Pleistocene period: Geol. Soc. Amer. Bull., vol. 44, p. 673, 1933.

and pulverizing action of the glacier. The material that is deposited by the meltwater from the ice is composed chiefly of gravel, sand, and silt and is assorted and more or less stratified.

The greater part of the drift in the Carlinville quadrangle is of Illinoian age. The loess overlying it is of Wisconsin age. At a few localities there are exposures of drift regarded as older than the Illinoian, and at other localities drift having some of the characteristics of the pre-Illinoian may represent only an early substage of the Illinoian stage. The drift regarded as pre-Illinoian is differentiated from the Illinoian because the two are separated by (1) humus horizons

PREGLACIAL SURFACE

The glacial deposits were laid down on a surface that apparently had about as much relief as that of the present average upland surface. The maximum relief of the bedrock surface (pl. 1) proved by well records is 152 feet—496 to 648 feet above sea level respectively in the NW ¼ NE ¼ sec. 17, T. 10 N., R. 7 W. (Carlinville Twp.) and at Modesto in the SW ¼ sec. 15, T. 12 N., R. 8 W. (North Palmyra Twp.). The higher elevations of the bedrock are in the north and northwest parts of the quadrangle.

One of the principal preglacial valleys, followed generally by the present valley of Otter Creek, along which the general absence of outcrops is significant, extends from northeast to southwest across the quadrangle. Another large valley, now generally

[1]Name first used in Lyell, Charles, Elements of geology, French translation, appendix, pp. 616-621, Paris, 1839. Also, Charlesworth's Magazine of Natural History, vol. 3, p. 323, footnote, 1839.
[2]Chamberlin, T. C., and Salisbury, R. D., Geology, vol. 1, p. 469, Henry Holt and Company, 1909.

PHOTO BY MAC CLINTOCK.

FIG. 16.—Humus zone underlying silt (probably Yarmouth floodplain deposits) and Illinoian till in the SE ¼ sec. 16, T. 11 N., R. 7 W. (South Otter Twp.) (geologic section 41).

filled with glacial drift, runs more nearly west from South Standard, near which it is joined by a fairly large tributary.

The glaciers advanced from the northeast, as is indicated by striae on the bedrock surface (table 5), which are thought to be related to the advance of the Illinoian glacier.

KANSAN STAGE[3]

Glacial drift more or less certainly of Kansan age has been noted at several localities in the Carlinville quadrangle (geologic sections 14, 38-45). In most exposures it is hard, dark gray, calcareous, somewhat pebbly till, and can be distinguished from the overlying Illinoian till principally because they are usually separated by sand, silt, and humus deposits believed to be of Yarmouth age. In a few exposures the upper part of the Kansan till is leached, the maximum depth of leaching as noted being 4½ feet (geologic section 38); this is considered evidence of its age as it lies beneath calcareous Yarmouth deposits or calcareous till of Illinoian age. The leached Kansan till is usually yellowish to reddish brown and gummy. The till is locally silty or sandy, and at some places it is associated with silt or sand beds as much as a foot thick. The maximum exposed thickness is 11 feet. Masses of this till are sometimes included in the lower part of the overlying Illinoian till.

Of unusual interest is the occurrence of distinct glacial striae on Kansan till in a stream bed in the SE ¼ SW ¼ sec. 14, T. 11 N., R. 8 W. (South Palmyra Twp.) (geologic section 44), subsequently concealed by the construction of a farm reservoir. The striae are straight, regular, uniformly parallel, and closely spaced. They trend S. 45° to 47° W. and are believed to have been made by the Illinoian glacier when it overrode the Kansan till in this region.

YARMOUTH STAGE[4]

Deposits that are regarded as Yarmouth in age occur at several localities in the Car-

[3]Named for the State of Kansas where it is widely distributed and is not overlain by younger glacial deposits. Chamberlin, T. C., in Geikie, James, The Great Ice Age, pp. 753-764, 1894. Chamberlin, T. C., The classification of American glacial deposits: Jour. Geology, vol. 3, pp. 270-277, 1895.

[4]Leverett, Frank, The weathered zone (Yarmouth) between the Illinoian and Kansan till sheets: Jour. Geol., vol. 6, pp. 238-243, 1898.

TABLE 5.—GLACIAL STRIAE

Location	Direction	Material
1. SE ¼ NE ¼ sec. 26, T. 10 N., R. 7. W.	S 63° W.	Shoal Creek limestone
2. NW ¼ SE ¼ sec. 30, T. 10 N., R. 7 W.	S. 47° W.	Carlinville limestone
3. NW ¼ NE ¼ sec. 34, T. 10 N., R. 6 W.	S. 40° W.	Shoal Creek limestone
4. SE ¼ SW ¼ sec. 14, T. 11 N., R. 8 W.	S. 45–47° W.	Pre-Illinoian till

TABLE 6.—YARMOUTH DEPOSITS IN THE CARLINVILLE QUADRANGLE

Geologic section	Locality	Summary of materials	Thickness Ft.	Thickness In.
39	SE ¼ NE ¼ sec. 30, T. 10 N., R. 6 W.	Sand, gravelly or silty	5	
		Humus		½
		Silt, with wood fragments		3–7
		Total	5	7½
40	Center of sec. 28, T. 10 N., R. 6 W.	Sand and silt	6	10
		Humus		6
		Total	7	4
41	NE ¼ SE ¼ sec. 16, T. 11 N., R. 7 W.	Silt or "fat" clay		3–6
		Humus		2–3
		Total		5–9
42	NW ¼ NW ¼ NE ¼ sec. 16, T. 11 N., R. 7 W.	Water-laid silt	2–3	
		Total	2–3	
43	NE ¼ SE ¼ sec. 9, T. 11 N., R. 7 W.	Silt		2–3
		Humus		1–2
		Silt	1	2
		Sand	1	2
		Total	2	9
46	SE ¼ SE ¼ sec. 10, T. 11 N., R. 7 W.	Clay		½
		Peat	2	4
		Silty peat	4	9
		Gravel		6–8+?
		Total	7	9½+?
47	NE ¼ sec. 27, T. 10 N., R. 7. W.	Sand and gravel	3	9½
		Humus		½
		Total	3	10

PHOTO BY NEEDHAM.

FIG. 17.—Yarmouth peat overlain by Illinoian till, in the SE ¼ sec. 10, T. 11 N., R. 7 W. (South Otter Twp.) (geologic section 46).

PHOTO BY NEEDHAM.

FIG. 18.—Yarmouth silt overlain by a humus band (marked in the photograph by a hammer), in turn overlain by sand, in the NE ¼ sec. 27, T. 10 N., R. 7 W. (Carlinville Twp.) (geologic section 47 and fig. 19).

linville quadrangle (geologic sections 39-43, 46, and 47, figs. 16-18, table 6). They appear to be comprised of three units: a bottom unit of fossiliferous dark gray carbonaceous or woody calcareous sandy silt 3 inches to 5 feet 5 inches thick, a middle unit of humus ½ inch to 6 inches thick or peat as much as 2 feet 4 inches thick, and a top unit of gray calcareous silt or fine-grained sand, grading laterally to "fat" clay, 2 inches to 6 feet 10 inches thick. Any one or two of these units may be lacking in some exposures, and at some places there are apparently no Yarmouth deposits between the Kansan and Illinoian tills (geologic sections 38, 44, 45).

The succession is typically exposed in a gully near Blackburn College at Carlinville (geologic section 47, figs. 18 and 19). Fossils occur and are frequently abundant in the bottom silt and middle humus units (Appendix C). The character of the materials and the type of fauna represented by the fossils indicate that the deposits are probably flood-plain deposits. At some places the upper silt-sand unit appears to grade upward or laterally into Illinoian till, which suggests that possibly some or all of the unit may be of Illinoian age—outwash deposited in front of the advancing Illinoian glacier.

ILLINOIAN STAGE[5]

Drift of Illinoian age occurs throughout the Carlinville quadrangle. Most of it is typical clay till, with numerous pebbles, several cobbles, and occasional boulders, but some of it is silt, sand, or gravel of glaciofluvial origin. The upper part of it, where it has been relatively undisturbed, has been more or less altered by weathering, and there are numerous places in the quadrangle where there are good examples of the profile of weathering[6] and of the gumbotil[7] that is typical of horizon 2 of this profile when developed on the older glacial tills. Because of the greater porosity of silt, sand, and gravel, the weathering seems to have progressed more rapidly where such material is near the surface of the Illinoian drift.

Exposures of typical Illinoian drift are frequent along the stream valleys in the west part of the quadrangle, especially in South Palmyra and Bird townships (geologic section 48). Silt, sand, and gravel occur together as pockets, lenses, or lenticular beds in the till, and in exposures in valley

[5]Named for the State of Illinois where it is best exposed. Chamberlin, T. C., Editorial: Jour. Geology, vol. 4, pp. 872-876, 1896.
[6]Leighton, M. M., and MacClintock, Paul, Weathered zones of the drift sheets of Illinois: Jour. Geol., vol. 37, pp. 28-53, 1929.
[7]Kay, G. F., and Pearce, J. Newton, The origin of gumbotil: Jour. Geol., vol. 28, pp. 89-125, 1920.

TABLE 7.—PEBBLE ANALYSIS OF THE ILLINOIAN TILL IN THE CARLINVILLE
AND ADJACENT QUADRANGLES

Name of Rock	LOCALITIES*								
	I	II		III		IV		V	
	Per-cent	No. of speci-mens	Per-cent	No. of speci-mens	Per-cent	No. of speci-mens	Per-cent	No. of speci-mens	Per-cent
Sedimentary									
Limestone, light...	31.6			9	9.28	18	12.2	28	20.6
Limestone, dark...		47	41.3	15	15.47	16	10.9		
Dolomite.........	6.4	25	21.9	4	4.12	51	34.7	52	38.2
Sandstone........	2.1	3	2.6	5	5.15	8	5.4	5	3.7
Shale............	2.9	2	1.8			7	4.8	6	4.4
Chert............	31.1	20	17.9	1	1.03	23	15.6	17	12.5
Quartz, round....	3.8	5	4.4			1	.7	3	2.3
Quartz, vein......	.4	1	.9			1	.7	2	1.5
Ironstone........	.8	1	.9					1	.7
Coal.............		1	.9					1	.7
Concretions......								8	5.9
Igneous									
Granite, pink.....	1.7	1	.9	6	6.19	1	.7	2	1.5
Granite, gray.....				6	6.19	1	.7		
Syenite..........				1	1.03				
Diorite..........	4.2			5	5.15	2	1.4	1	.7
Basalt...........	2.5					4	2.7	1	.7
Felsite..........	2.1	1	.9	1	1.03			1	.7
Greenstone.......	4.2	1	.9	6	6.19				
Gabbro..........				7	7.22				
Diabase..........		2	1.8	1	1.03				
Rhyolite.........				1	1.03	1	.7		
Trachyte.........				1	1.03				
Granite, gneiss....				3	3.09				
Pegmatite........				2	2.06				
Andesite.........				1	1.03				
Peridotite........						2	1.4		
Metamorphic									
Quartzite........	3.4	3	2.6	6	6.19	5	3.4		
Graywacke.......						1	.7	5	3.7
Gneiss...........				10	10.31	1	.7		
Schist...........		1	.9	6	6.19	4	2.7	3	2.2
Arkos-argillite....	2.1								
Totals.........	99.3	114	100.6	97	100.01	147	100.1	136	100.0

*Key to localities:
I — SE ¼ sec. 16, T. 11 N., R. 7 W. Number of pebbles not recorded.
II — NE ¼ sec. 33, T. 11 N., R. 6 W.
III — SW ¼ sec. 2, T. 9 N., R. 7 W.
IV — NW ¼ sec. 27, T. 10 N., R. 7 W.
V — NE ¼ sec. 28, T. 9 N., R. 8 W.

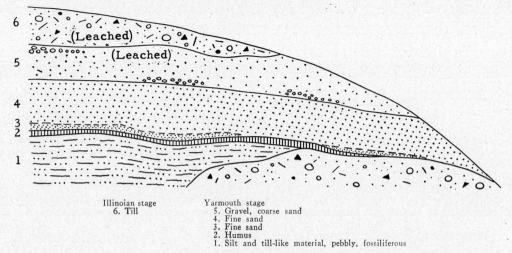

Illinoian stage	Yarmouth stage
6. Till	5. Gravel, coarse sand
	4. Fine sand
	3. Fine sand
	2. Humus
	1. Silt and till-like material, pebbly, fossiliferous

FIG. 19.—Sketch showing relationships of Illinoian till and Yarmouth deposits near Blackburn College (geologic section 47 and fig. 18).

walls and slopes they are responsible for seepage and springs. It is more common in the eastern part of the quadrangle, where the character of the drift may show considerable variation in short distances (geologic section 49).

There are numerous places along the valleys in the quadrangle where as much as 50 to 70 feet of Illinoian drift is exposed, and along Otter Creek in the northern part of sec. 26, T. 11 N., R. 8 W. (South Palmyra Twp.) 90 feet is exposed. Records of borings in the quadrangle report glacial drift 100 to 190 feet thick. The greatest thicknesses record the presence of valleys in the bedrock surface, presumably preglacial in age, and thus may include pre-Illinoian as well as Illinoian drift.

Pebbles collected from the Illinoian drift at a few localities in and near the Carlinville quadrangle were identified in order to ascertain the relative abundance of the various rock types (table 7). The character of these collections is sufficiently different from collections from Kansan drift[8] to be a criterion for the differentiation of the two drifts. It also indicates the rocks from which the till was derived.

Boulders are not very common in the drift. Except in the valley of Hurricane

Creek boulders more than one foot in greatest diameter are relatively few. A few of the larger erratics observed in the quadrangle have been listed (table 8); all but one are of rock types that occur in Canada, thus revealing the distant sources of the drift.

In addition to the silt, sand, and gravel intimately associated with the till, more segregated deposits of glacio-fluvial material of Illinoian age occur in the Carlinville quadrangle as follows: 1.) Although the upper part of Coops Mound seems to consist of till mantled with loess, the presence of gumbogravel about 50 feet above Macoupin Creek indicates that from that horizon downward the basal part of the mound consists wholly or largely of sand and gravel, interpreted as a deposit in a fissure or crevasse in the glacier. 2.) Shallow test borings near the Carlinville waterworks indicate that in a pre-Illinoian valley 29 to 36 feet below the terrace in Macoupin Valley there is coarse gravel below Illinoian till. It is interpreted as outwash from the advancing Illinoian glacier or as deposits in a subglacial channel in the glacier. 3.) The moderately fine gravels in the terraces along Macoupin Creek are believed to be outwash material deposited by the meltwaters from the glacier when its margin stood at the position now marked by the Jacksonville moraine.

[8]MacClintock, Paul, Correlation of the pre-Illinoian drifts of Illinois: Jour. Geol., vol. 41, pp. 715-716, 1933.

TABLE 8.—OCCURRENCE OF LARGE BOULDER ERRATICS IN THE
CARLINVILLE QUADRANGLE

Kind of Rock	Locality			Size in inches	Remarks
	sec.	T.	R.		
1. Gabbro..............	SE ¼	35	10 N. 7 W.	42x25x27	Associated with smaller pink granites
2. Gabbro..............	SE ¼	4	9 N. 7 W.	18x18x13	This, and the following granite, associated with another gabbro not measured
3. Pink granite.........	(same as No. 2)			24x16x11	
4. Pink rhyolite........	NE ¼	34	11 N. 8 W.	?	
5. Red sandstone.......	NW ¼	34	11 N 8 W.	53x29x20	Contains jasper pebbles
6. Biotite-granite.......	SE ¼	25	10 N. 7 W.	51x54x50	
7. Carlinville limestone...	SE ¼	34	10 N. 8 W.	135x102x51	
8. Gabbro..............	SE ¼	30	10 N. 7 W.	73x72x43	Valley of Hurricane Creek

SANGAMON STAGE[9]

Sangamon deposits are not conspicuous in the Carlinville quadrangle. They are associated with deposits of Wisconsin or Illinoian age (geologic section 50) and consist of peat and marl.

WISCONSIN STAGE[10]

During the Wisconsin stage of glaciation loess deposits were extensively distributed over the Carlinville quadrangle. They comprise both the Farmdale[11] (formerly called

[9]Named for Sangamon County, Ill., where first studied, and because of its conspicuous development in the drainage basin of Sangamon River. Worthen, A. H., Geology of Sangamon County: Geol. Survey of Illinois, vol. 5, p. 307, 1873. Leverett, Frank, The Illinois glacial lobe: U. S. Geol. Survey Monograph 38, p. 125, 1899.

[10]Named for the State of Wisconsin where the drift is widely distributed. Chamberlin, T. C., *in* Geikie, James, The Great Ice Age, 3rd ed., pp. 754-775, 1894. Chamberlin, T. C., The classification of American glacial deposits: Jour. Geology, vol. 3, pp. 270-277, 1895.

[11]Named for the village of Farmdale, Peoria County, Ill., near which are exposures that establish the stratigraphic and time relations of the loess. Leighton, M. M., and Willman, H. B., Late Cenozoic geology of Mississippi Valley: Itinerary Field Conference, auspices of State Geologist, printed by Illinois State Geological Survey, p. 7 (table 1) *et seq.*, 1949; Leighton, M. M., and Willman, H. B., Loess formations of Mississippi Valley (abst.): Geol. Soc. Amer. Bull., vol. 60, pp. 1904-05, 1949; Jour. Geol., vol. 58, pp. 602-03, 1950; reprinted as Illinois Geol. Survey Rept. Inv. 149. Also cited in Wascher, H. L., Humbert, R. P., and Cady, J. G., Loess in the southern Mississippi Valley; identification and distribution of the loess sheets: Soil Sci. Soc. Amer. Proc. (1947), vol. 12, p. 390, 1948, and in Horberg, Leland, Ground-water in the Peoria region: Illinois Geol. Survey Bull. 75 (Illinois Water Survey Bull. 39), p. 29, 1950.

Late Sangamon) and the Peorian[12] loesses. Although not distributed uniformly over the quadrangle, they are distributed over the uplands in sufficient thickness to conceal any boulder erratics that lay on the surface of the Illinoian drift. Along the course of Hurricane Creek, they have not been distinguished clearly from abundant silts and clays that are associated with the glaciofluvial deposits laid down along the lines of the preglacial drainage that cross this central part of the quadrangle (pl. 1).

Along a road leading out of the valley of Bear Creek, SE ¼ sec. 6, T. 10 N., R. 7 W. (Carlinville Twp.), 5 or 6 feet of dark brown leached Farmdale loess or silt is intermediate between the upland and the valley floor. The same material is in the banks of the creek, 10 or 20 feet lower. Some pebbles show near the base of this deposit, however, and in part it may be flood-plain or slope-wash deposit.

The Peorian loess is thickest near the principal valleys, and in some places, especially in the eastern and southeastern parts of the quadrangle, it seemingly is absent.

[12]Leverett, Frank, The Peorian soil and weathered zone (Toronto formation ?): Jour. Geol., vol. 6, pp. 244-249, 1898. Kay, George F., and Leighton, M. M., Eldoran epoch of the Pleistocene period: Bull. Geol. Soc. Amer., vol. 44, p. 673, 1933.

It is abundant in the terraces along Macoupin Creek, east and southeast of Carlinville, where it is as much as 10 feet thick (geologic section 53). It was also deposited on the uplands for a short distance east of Macoupin Creek — it is exposed along State Highway 108 in a relatively thin bed (geologic section 52) — but farther south and east it is not conspicuous on the uplands.

Northeast of Carlinville, it appears along the Chicago and North Western Railway near Coops Mound, sec. 19, T. 10 N., R. 6 W. In the cut of an east-west road that crosses the southern end of the mound, the Peorian loess overlies about 1½ feet of Farmdale loess. Farther west, in the southeastern part of South Palmyra township, the Peorian loess is exposed in cuts of the highway that approaches Otter Creek between secs. 25 and 26 (geologic section 55).

On the uplands this loess is associated with light ash-colored "forest soils." It commonly is a light yellow-gray pebble-free material which stands more or less vertically in road cuts. Where thoroughly oxidized it is a uniform brown and in many instances yellowish gray mottled with brown, possibly due to the weathering of small limonite or manganese concretions that at some localities have been noted in place. In thickness the Peorian loess ranges up to 11 or 12 feet (geologic sections 53 and 54) and averages about 6 feet.

RECENT STAGE

The most recent geologic deposit in the quadrangle is the alluvium laid down in the stream beds and on the valley floors of all the principal streams, slope wash on the valley walls, and eolian dust. In these places various types of soils[13] have developed and produce an accumulation of partly de-

[13]Norton *et al.*, Macoupin County Soils, Univ. of Ill. Agri. Exp. Sta., Soil Report No. 50, Urbana, 1932.

cayed organic matter which constitutes a further deposit.

The material of the alluvium varies from gravel and coarse sand to a fine-grained dark mealy silt. The sand and gravel sometimes underlie the finer material, interposed between that and the bedrock, and in other instances compose the surface deposits of the flood plains. The sand and gravel frequently are in pockets in the finer material. Sand and gravel are conspicuous along Hurricane Creek, west of Carlinville, upstream and downstream from the bridge of State Highway 108. In the valley of this stream some of the alluvial deposits occur in terraces and probably are glaciofluvial deposits reworked by recent stream action. The "bronzed" or coated pebbles mentioned earlier (page 45) are conspicuous in the alluvial gravels east of Carlinville in the valley of Macoupin Creek. Elsewhere the coarse material is in numerous sand and gravel bars like those in low waters. Great amounts of gravel and sand are deposited along the lower reaches of Bear Creek in the western part of the quadrangle and in the beds of Anderson and Richardson creeks in the eastern part of the quadrangle.

The finer alluvial deposits are silty, noncalcareous, and commonly dark gray and stand in vertical walls along the stream channels. The alluvium is locally crossbedded and frequently carries inclusions of coarse material. Other inclusions, in large holes or pockets, are almost soil in composition, and may be driftwood deposits thoroughly altered by decomposition and bacterial action. Fine silty alluvium is most common in the valleys of the smaller streams.

The thickness of the alluvium is variable. In Burroughs Branch, east of Carlinville, it is 7 feet thick.

CHAPTER VI — STRUCTURAL GEOLOGY

Marine sediments, when first deposited, normally form horizontal or nearly horizontal beds. However, they do not remain always in level or gently sloping positions; as a result of the earth's forces which cause movements of its crust they may be folded or faulted, that is, ruptured and displaced. That phase of geology dealing with the attitude of the rocks and with the interpretation of the crustal movements which brought them into that attitude is known as *structural geology*.

The geologic structure of a region may be depicted by a structural contour map which consists of contour lines drawn on the surface of any distinct and persistent stratum or key bed to show its elevation with reference to sea level. The degree of accuracy of such a map of course depends on the number of points at which the elevation can be determined.

A structure map of the Carlinville quadrangle (pl. 3)[1] has been drawn on the top of the Herrin (No. 6) coal, which is reported in the records of most of the borings in the quadrangle. Other prominent coal beds and older formations that might be used as key beds are so deeply buried and shown in so few records that there are insufficient datum points to provide a satisfactory structure map.

As indicated on this map, the coal bed dips or slopes generally eastward, if local irregularities are disregarded. This is in accordance with the fact that the Carlinville quadrangle lies in the western part of the Illinois basin, the broad structural depression that includes almost all of Illinois except the north end and includes adjacent parts of Indiana and Kentucky.[2] Names have been applied already to many of the local folds shown on the map,[3] and others are hereafter proposed.

Because the datum points are more numerous, the structure of this coal bed is depicted in more detail in the eastern part of the quadrangle. In general the coal descends gradually towards the southeast to a pronounced structural basin or trough of irregular outline, somewhat resembling a clover leaf, in the west part of T. 10 N., R. 6 W. (Shaw Point Twp.). It descends from 478 feet above sea level at Modesto to 285 feet in the test boring at the southwest end of the artificial lake at Schoper, in the NW ¼ sec. 8, T. 10 N., R. 6 W. (Shaw Point Twp.), a total of 193 feet, which amounts to an average of about 14 feet per mile.

The local folds in the eastern part of the quadrangle comprise a radial series of low, broad uplifts or anticlines and alternating depressions or synclines, most of which converge and plunge in the general direction of Coops Mound. The northeasternmost fold of this structure is a syncline, herein named the Greenridge syncline because the Greenridge mine and the village of Greenridge are located near its axis, which lies between Nilwood and Girard. It apparently extends from near the center of T. 12 N., R. 7 W. (North Otter Twp.) to the center of the west line of T. 11 N., R. 5 W. (Pitman Twp.) in the Raymond quadrangle. Near Girard the trough of this syncline plunges gently S. 45° E., but as it leaves the quadrangle its plunge is more directly eastward. In the Girard mine, on the northeast limb of this syncline, the coal is at an elevation of 327 feet, whereas in the Greenridge mine shaft, slightly southwest of the trough, it is 328 feet above sea level. West of Girard, in a distance of 1½ miles, the coal rises to an elevation of 363 feet above sea level.

The Greenridge syncline is separated from the next structural depression to the southwest by the Nilwood anticline,[4] which plunges southeast and south. The coal in the Nilwood mine shaft is 57 feet above its elevation at Providence Church, in the SE ¼ sec. 25, T. 11 N., R. 6 W. (Nilwood

[1]This map differs from that published in Illinois Geol. Survey Circ. 88 only in minor details to accord with data obtained after the preparation of that publication.
[2]Structure maps showing this basin have been included in numerous publications of the Illinois State Geological Survey and elsewhere.
[3]Easton, William H., Oil and gas possibilities, *in* Structure of Herrin (No. 6) coal bed in Macoupin County, etc.: Illinois Geol. Survey Circ. 88, pp. 28-33, 1942.
[4]Easton, *op. cit.*, p. 33.

TABLE 9.—JOINTS IN BEDROCK IN THE CARLINVILLE QUADRANGLE

LOCALITY				Direction of joints		Geologic formation	Geologic section
T.N.	R.W.	Sec.	¼ sec.				
12	8	34	SE, NE	N. 62° E.	N. 36° W.	Carlinville ls.	8
11	7	16	NW, NE	N. 57° E.	N. 36° W.	Shoal Creek ls.	36
10	6	22	NW, SW	N. 70–75° E.		Shoal Creek ls.	..
10	7	30	SE	N. 70° E.	N. 28° W.	Carlinville ls.	..
10	7	35	West ½ NE, NW	W. 65° E.	N. 25° W.	Carlinville ls.	15
9	7	4	NW, SE	N. 65–70° E.	N. 20–30° W.	Carlinville ls.	..

Twp.), in the Raymond quadrangle. This is a difference of about 9 feet to the mile, a little less than the average regional dip of the coal. Data for the elevations of the coal northwest of Nilwood are lacking, but it is assumed that the axis of the anticline persists as far northwest into North Otter Township as the trough of the Greenridge syncline is drawn.

The closed end of another gently plunging syncline is outlined by the contours south and west of Nilwood. The trough of this syncline trends S. 30° E. as it passes south of Nilwood, but at South Standard it turns abruptly south. The elevation of the coal is 331 feet east of Hickory Point School, in sec. 14, T. 11 N., R. 7 W. (South Otter Twp.), 303 feet in a test boring north of South Standard, and 285 feet west of Schoper, making an average plunge of about 10 feet per mile.

The other three anticlines in the radial pattern are broadly triangular structures, and the two synclines are narrow and somewhat trough-like. The elevation of the coal on the Anderson anticline[5] west of South Standard is about the same as it is on the Nilwood anticline. The broad Burton anticline[6] is similar in outline to the Anderson, but the coal in the Weir shaft is about 30 feet higher than in similarly located areas on the Nilwood and Anderson anticlines. The axis of the Burton anticline trends a little south of east under Carlinville and then turns northeastward, forming the most pronounced anticlinal structure in the quadrangle. The faintly defined northeast

end of the Carlinville anticline[7] crosses the southeast corner of the quadrangle with its axis running almost due north.

The structural depression between the Anderson and Burton anticlines resembles the other synclines in the quadrangle, but its trough trends in a nearly straight course S. 60° E. Its direction of plunge is nearly at right angles to the direction of the other syncline, herein named the Sugar Creek syncline because its axis almost coincides with Sugar Creek, which trends N. 30° E. East of Coops Mound, there is only one broad shallow trough.

MINOR STRUCTURAL FEATURES

Fault in the Girard mine. — In 1892 the Girard Colliery discovered near the south line of its property a fault whose strike varied from N. 55° W. to N. 30° W. The vertical displacement was such that no trace of the coal could be discovered on the far side of the fault for a distance of 15 feet either above or below the level of the bed in the mine.[8] The conclusion reached by the mine engineers was that the downthrow of the fault was on the south side, because in an exploratory tunnel they found a thick limestone that was thought to be the limestone overlying the coal.

Joints. — In connection with the movements which rocks undergo as one result of the earth forces, they are generally more or less fractured. These fractures are most prominent in the firmer rocks, such as lime-

[5]Easton, *op. cit.*, p. 29.
[6]Easton, *op. cit.*, p. 29.

[7]Name originally applied only to part of the structure. Kay, Fred, The Carlinville oil and gas field: Illinois Geol. Survey Bull. 20, Yearbook for 1910, p. 92, 1915.
[8]Young, Hiram, The fault at Girard: Jour. Illinois Min. Inst., vol. 1, pp. 194-196, 2 diagrams, 1892.

stones, sandstones, and hard shales, where they usually appear as two sets of parallel joints at nearly right angles. This double system of joints has been observed at numerous places in the Carlinville quadrangle and is especially well developed at some localities (table 9).

Minor folds. — The general structure of the bedrock in the Carlinville quadrangle, even on the local folds, is so moderate that the rock strata usually appear to be horizontal, although in some places, where outcrops occur on the sides or ends of the anticline, dips of 1-2° may be measured. In a few places in the quadrangle slight reversals of dips within short horizontal distances give rise to visible slight undulations or "rolls." Under the Broad Street bridge in Carlinville the Carlinville limestone dips 1-2° N. 35° E., but a few rods downstream the dip is reversed. In sec. 35, T. 10 N., R. 7 W. (Carlinville Twp.) the limestone

is exposed at stream level along Macoupin Creek both in the northwest quarter and near the southwest corner of the section, but between these points several feet of the underlying shale is also exposed.

Another minor fold probably accounts for the reappearance, upstream, of the black platy shale which underlies the Macoupin limestone in the gully containing the typical exposures for the quadrangle (geologic sections 19 and 20). In sec. 34, T. 12 N., R. 8 W. (North Palmyra Twp.) (geologic section 8), the Carlinville limestone that forms the waterfall ledge has an upstream dip, although the general structure is in the opposite direction. At the same locality the shale and sandstone that underlie the limestone downstream from the waterfall ledge have been forced into a small asymmetrical overturned fold, whose axis is inclined to the west and which passes upward into a reverse fault with the upthrow on the east.

CHAPTER VII — GEOLOGIC HISTORY

INTRODUCTION

Geologic time is divided into five major divisions or eras, which are further subdivided successively into periods, epochs, subepochs, stages, etc. As has been pointed out, only the Pennsylvanian period of the Paleozoic era and the Pleistocene period of the Cenozoic era are represented by the rocks that crop out in the Carlinville quadrangle. Wells in the quadrangle penetrate and provide information about formations belonging to the Mississippian, Devonian, Silurian, and Ordovician periods of the Paleozoic era. The geologic history of the quadrangle with regard to the other periods and eras must be inferred from information obtained elsewhere.

PRE-PALEOZOIC ERAS

Rocks of the two oldest geologic eras, the Archeozoic and the Proterozoic, do not crop out in Illinois and have been encountered in only a few wells. From these wells it is inferred that these oldest rocks in Illinois are similar to those outcropping in the Missouri Ozarks and elsewhere, where they consist of igneous and highly metamorphosed rocks.

Many of the metamorphic rocks were originally sedimentary, indicating that in the early geologic eras there were periods when the region was submerged. The presence of granite and the highly metamorphic state of the old rocks is evidence that during the pre-Paleozoic eras the region was also subjected to vulcanism and major mountain-making earth movements.

Immediately preceding the Paleozoic era there was a long period of erosion over an extensive land surface. On this surface were deposited the sediments of the Cambrian period.

PALEOZOIC ERA

CAMBRIAN PERIOD

Although in the early part of the Cambrian period, sea water entered far inland along the Pacific and Atlantic coastal regions of North America, it did not enter the Mississippi Valley region until the late Cambrian or St. Croixan epoch. Then the interior of the continent was inundated, and a succession of sandstone, shale, and calcareous deposits was laid down during stages of submergence of the land, interrupted by temporary withdrawal of the seas. At the end of the Cambrian period, there was a long period of uplift and erosion.

ORDOVICIAN PERIOD

Like the last epoch of the Cambrian period, the Ordovician period in central North America was marked principally by marine submergence, with only two or three withdrawals of any consequence. At the beginning of the Chazyan epoch there began a slow transgression of the sea over the interior regions of the continent, a transgression that was one of the most extensive of all geologic time. According to the latest interpretation,[1] shoreward deposits of this transgression were sands that now constitute the St. Peter sandstone, which is widely distributed throughout the Mississippi Valley region, and successive portions of which were contemporaneous with the calcareous deposits that now constitute the Dutchtown, Joachim, and Plattin formations. At the close of Plattin time, and possibly continuing into the beginning of Galena (Kimmswick) time, the deposits grew more muddy and sandy as indicated by the intermingled Decorah shales and limestones of the Mohawkian epoch. Then the Galena (Kimmswick) limestone was deposited during a long period of time. The sea which received these limy sediments was not necessarily very deep, as the limestone in places is cross-bedded.[2] The limestone is slightly dolomitic, which may be due to a change in composition after induration.

---

[1]Du Bois, E. P., Subsurface relations of the Maquoketa and "Trenton" formations in Illinois: Illinois Geol. Survey Rept. Inv. 105, pp. 32-33, 1945.

[2]Weller, Stuart, Geology of Ste. Genevieve County, Missouri: Missouri Bureau Geol. and Mines, vol. 22, 2nd Series, p. 289, 1928.

CINCINNATIAN EPOCH

Maquoketa stage

A wide emergence of the land ended the Mohawkian epoch. The shales and calcareous muds of the Maquoketa formation indicate more shallow waters and muddier seas than in the Mohawkian epoch. In about the middle of the Maquoketa stage, however, the sea became clear, and deposition of limy sediments continued for some time. Later, the deposition of argillaceous muds and silts was resumed. The Cincinnatian epoch was terminated by uplift and emergence, followed by erosion of the Maquoketa formation.[3]

SILURIAN PERIOD

ALEXANDRIAN EPOCH

Edgewood stage

Calcareous mud deposited in the sea during the Edgewood stage of the Alexandrian epoch is now cherty dolomite. In the vicinity of Palmyra, deposits which have formed oolitic limestone were laid down. Toward the close of the Edgewood stage, the region of the Ozark Mountains was slightly tilted before the Sexton Creek deposits were laid down. Other than this very slight crustal movement, no appreciable change in conditions seems to have occurred between the Edgewood and the Sexton Creek stages.

Sexton Creek stage

The land slowly resubmerged, and a possibly larger area was covered by the sea during the deposition of the Sexton Creek sediments. Late Alexandrian (Brassfield) sedimentary rocks are traceable from eastern Ohio to Arkansas. The equivalent Kankakee formation extends northward through Illinois and Iowa into Wisconsin and the Great Lakes region. Just as it is formed in the seas of today, glauconite was deposited in the Sexton Creek sediments of the Carlinville quadrangle in notable amounts. Glauconite is a hydrous silicate of potassium, aluminum, and iron; it is flaky, opaque, and vividly green, and is commonly believed to indicate exceedingly

[3]Du Bois, op. cit., p. 14.

slow deposition. Thus the Sexton Creek stage possibly was of long duration, although the formation is only slightly more than 20 feet thick. Slight uplift terminated the Alexandrian epoch.

NIAGARAN EPOCH

The Ozark region was uplifted at the end of the Alexandrian epoch, but the southern sea in which most of the Alexandrian sediments were deposited came back into the region during the Clinton stage. Both the late Alexandrian sediments and the early Niagaran sediments in the lower Mississippi Valley and elsewhere are pinkish or reddish, evidently due to oxidation of iron compounds in them.

CAYUGAN EPOCH

During the Cayugan (late Silurian) epoch the region was either a land area and no deposits were made or, if there were marine deposits, they were later entirely eroded.

DEVONIAN PERIOD

Wapsipinicon stage

The history of Devonian times within the quadrangle is recorded by only two formations, both of Middle Devonian age. The great erosional unconformity separating the Wapsipinicon formation from the Silurian rocks beneath it indicates a long passage of time, probably the Cayugan epoch of the Silurian period and the Helderbergian and Oriskanian epochs of the Devonian period. The Devonian sea which was advancing from the south inundated the eastern Ozarks region long before it reached the Carlinville area. Evidently at that time the Carlinville area was a low-lying land contributing limy sediments and minerals to the Devonian sea.

Deposits during the Wapsipinicon stage were chiefly sediments which now are limestone and dolomite, but sandy grains suggest that the shoreline of that time possibly was not very far distant. Sands which were later washed into the sea in greater amount reflect the movements which occurred in the Ozarks region at about that time. Finally, a complete uplift came, and the Carlinville region was extensively eroded.

Cedar Valley stage

The sea returned again in the Middle Devonian, and although sedimentation was extensive elsewhere in the Mississippi Valley, the rocks of the Cedar Valley formation are extremely restricted in the Carlinville area. The basal part of the formation as it was developed here is sandy. Following the deposition of the basal sandstone in the Cedar Valley formation the seas cleared somewhat, and calcareous deposits were laid down. Then deposition was terminated by uplift, and erosion was widespread prior to the advance of the Mississippian sea.

MISSISSIPPIAN PERIOD
KINDERHOOK SUBEPOCH

Grassy Creek stage

The early deposits of the Mississippian system in the Mississippi Valley are black and brown shales which extend from the Appalachian Mountains to Oklahoma. They point possibly to the presence of thick black soils on the adjacent lands[4] or may represent colloidal material carried from low lands.[5]

Louisiana stage

The deposition of the black shale was followed, without interruption apparently, by the deposition of the Louisiana limestone which is of limited extent in the quadrangle and in this part of Illinois. The formation of the Louisiana limestone took place during continued submergence of the area, with better conditions prevailing locally for marine forms of life than were known during the accumulation of the dark muds of the Grassy Creek stage.

Hannibal stage

A slight upward warping with some emergence followed the deposition of the Louisiana limestone. There is even evidence of some erosion at the top of the Louisiana limestone. Then the re-advancing sea became muddy again, and the Hannibal shales were deposited.

Hamburg-Maple Mill substages. — The

lower, and by far the thicker, part of the Hannibal deposits is a shaly sandstone which was laid down during the Hamburg substage. Some siltstone and some pure shales were intermingled. Locally in the basal portion of these clastic deposits an oolitic limestone was formed. Oolites form under so many conditions that their occurrence here indicates merely the presence of warm and relatively shallow waters with plenty of wave motion prevailing. Conditions for deposition of shale and siltstone were then renewed, and on these sediments, without any cessation of deposition, about 15 feet of Maple Mill shale and siltstone were laid down.

Chouteau stage

After the Maple Mill substage the Kinderhook seas cleared so completely that a very pure limestone with only some traces of silt, the Chouteau formation, was deposited. Some glauconite occurs in the limestone, which is an indication, possibly, of a long period of deposition of calcareous muds.

OSAGE SUBEPOCH

An uplift terminated the Kinderhook epoch and subjected at least a part of the lower Mississippi Valley to erosion before the Osage epoch.

Fern Glen stage

The period of emergence probably was long, as the deep red of the Fern Glen beds is thought to be due to a red residual clay developed by long oxidation on the surface and supplied in considerable amount to the Fern Glen sea,[6] but not enough to vitiate the abundant life in its waters.

Burlington-Keokuk stages

The thick deposits of limestone that followed in the Burlington and Keokuk times are an indication of clearing seas and of conditions favorable for prolific life. Limestone deposition was interrupted possibly by slight local uplifts and warping because lenticular masses of sandstone are inter-

[4]Moore, R. C., Historical Geology: McGraw-Hill Book Co.. Inc., p. 274, 1933.
[5]Weller, J. Marvin, and Sutton, A. H., Mississippian border of Eastern Illinois Basin: Amer. Assn. Petr. Geol. Bull., vol. 24, p. 789, 1940. Reprinted as Illinois Geol. Survey Rept. Inv. 62.

[6]Weller, Stuart, The geology of Ste. Genevieve County Missouri: Missouri Bur. Geol. and Mines, vol. XXII, 2nd ser., p. 301, 1928.

bedded with the calcareous deposits. These sandstones, however, may be merely lenticular deposits of sand reaching in from the east and mingling with the calcareous deposits from the west. A vast submergence affected the midcontinental area at this time, the Mississippian limestones extending from the southern Appalachians to regions west of the Rocky Mountains. The Ozarks, on whose northern flanks the earlier Mississippian sediments were deposited, were entirely submerged. The cherts of the Burlington are distributed entirely across the region, and Mississippian faunas east and west of the present Ozarks are similar.

Warsaw stage

Probably the submerged area was somewhat reduced in extent by an uplift in the late Osage epoch because at the base of the Warsaw strata there are locally sands and shales more than 70 feet in thickness. Here, again, the sands may mean only local deposits washed into deeper waters by strong storm waves. The Ozarks, however, were uplifted slightly at this time, and during oscillatory substages supplied considerable sand and mud to the sea.

MERAMEC SUBEPOCH

Salem stage

During the Salem stage, practically nothing but calcareous muds were laid down in the sea, but a pronounced crustal movement elevated some of the southern Mississippi Valley above the sea, and there was a cessation of deposition between the Salem and St. Louis stages.

St. Louis and Ste. Genevieve stages

After the partial interruption caused by local and slight uplifts with the appearance of coarser sediments, a further deepening of the seas made possible the deposition of the St. Louis and Ste. Genevieve limestones, after which there was uplift, warping, and erosion.

CHESTER EPOCH[7]

The Carlinville quadrangle area was submerged again in the Chester epoch. The

typical Chester alternation of sandstone (or shale) and limestone formations is indicative of regularly oscillating conditions.

PENNSYLVANIAN PERIOD
CASEYVILLE AND TRADEWATER SUBEPOCHS

The Mississippian period was terminated by an uplift of the land that tilted the Carlinville area eastward, and a long period of erosion followed. Although most of North America was land at the beginning of the Pennsylvanian period, most of the interior consisted of lowland basins in which more or less local deposition, both continental and marine, occurred in cyclical sequence.

The deposits of the early part of the Caseyville subepoch are in large measure continental and probably were laid down under a number of different conditions. Sandstones, either channel fillings, alluvial plains, or marine offshore bars, are prevalent. Coals, indicative of swamp conditions, and limestones, indicative of marine conditions, are present.

It may be that the streams were eroding vigorously in their upper reaches and carrying sediments into the lower part of the drainage systems, where they aggraded their channels and spread out deposits over the lowlands. Shifting channels and bars, along with local downwarpings, converted some of the lowlands into basins and swamps in which vegetation accumulated to form peat, later to become coal. Extensive deposits of black shale above the coal beds indicate that these peat-filled basins were gradually flooded by marine waters, in which there accumulated deposits of calcareous shales and limy sediments as the waters deepened.

CARBONDALE SUBEPOCH

In general, cyclic deposition prevailed during the Carbondale epoch although conditions necessary to produce the basal sandstones did not occur often. Following the Liverpool cycle there was a definite episode of channel cutting, as the earliest deposit of the Summum cycle is a channel sandstone, the Pleasantview, recognized widely in Illinois.

[7]Workman, L. E., Subsurface geology of the Chester series in Illinois: Amer. Assn. Petr. Geol. Bull., vol. 24, fig. 1, p. 210, 1940.

Saint David cycle

As most of the members of the Saint David cycle are marine, the continental phase of the cycle was apparently not well developed. The thickness of the Herrin (No. 6) coal indicates that the swamp forest from which it is derived probably existed for several thousands of years.[8] The accumulation of carbonaceous matter in the swamp was interrupted at least once by the introduction of a notable amount of clay, which constitutes the "blue band" characteristic of this coal bed. The widespread distribution of the Brereton limestone or its equivalent indicates that at that time marine waters lay over wide areas for a long time. Channeling and erosion of the Herrin (No. 6) coal south of Carlinville[9] may be attributed to uplift that terminated the Carbondale subepoch.

McLEANSBORO SUBEPOCH

Jamestown and Bankston Fork cycles

Both the Jamestown and Bankston Fork cyclothems indicate incomplete cycles of deposition and suggest that the conditions of deposition changed frequently. Probably a great deal of the land was just above sea level, although coal formed in only a few localities. Later, however, the Bankston Fork limestone was formed over a wide area, and the sea stood over much, if not all, of the Carlinville quadrangle for a long time.

Sparland cycle

The Sparland cycle was initiated by slight uplift, a sandy shale frequently appearing at the base of the cyclothem. Locally in the low-lying surfaces of the area the underclay was developed, the land became swampy, and in the swamp grew forest from which the Danville (No. 7) coal was formed. Later the sea entered the region, and the Sparland limestone was laid down over large areas. The transition back to land conditions through gradually shoaling waters was evidently slow, as the marine shale uppermost in the cyclothem is very thick in places.

Gimlet cycle

During the Gimlet cycle the region around Carlinville must have been swampy, as indicated by the 5-foot bed of the Gimlet coal in the Weir mine shaft. The latter part of the Gimlet cycle is represented by extensive shale deposits instead of a marine limestone (the Lonsdale limestone, as it is known elsewhere).

Scottville cycle

The coal of the Scottville cycle, never thick, is a mere horizon or trace in the Carlinville quadrangle, but the Scottville limestone is prominent and fairly widespread.

Trivoli cycle

Continental conditions must have prevailed for some time during the early part of the Trivoli cycle because sandstone and shale of notable thickness occur under the coal. Coal and black shale, indicative of swamp and marsh conditions, and leached underclays, believed to be indicative of surficial weathering, are present. In some records thicknesses of this underclay have probably been exaggerated.

Some incursion of the sea is recorded during the Trivoli cycle by slight thicknesses of dark shale and the presence of a few fossils. The seas did not become very deep or clear, however, as the deposits are dominantly shales, and but little limestone is found.

Carlinville cycle

Relative elevation evidently closed the Trivoli and ushered in the Carlinville cycle[10] because, in addition to the basal sandstone, there is evidence that at one or two localities a channel sandstone of considerable thickness belongs in the cyclothem. The development of typical underclays and coal did not occur to any marked extent, although thin coal seams are found. Some black shale, bearing abundant fern leaves, is associated with the lower ledge of the Carlinville limestone, and its commonly dark color is suggestive of plentiful plant material either

---

[8]Ashley, G. H., The maximum rate of deposition of coal: Econ. Geol., vol. 2, p. 45, 1907.

[9]Kay, F. H., Coal resources of District VII: Illinois Geol. Survey Coop. Min. Ser. Bull. 11, p. 95, 1916.

[10]The Collinsville, recognized elsewhere in the southwestern part of the state, is tentatively recognized in the Raymond quadrangle, east of the Carlinville quadrangle.

in the sea or derived from the freshwater swamps. The inundation evidently was widespread and of long duration, as the Carlinville limestone is one of the thickest exposed in the quadrangle, and its distribution is fully as extensive as any of the several limestones in the southern part of the state. That the cycle closed slowly is indicated by a shale fully 15 feet in thickness bearing ironstone concretions, which covers the limestone in the southern part of Carlinville and along Macoupin Creek, east of the city.

Burroughs beds deposition.—Only a slight change of conditions terminated the Carlinville cycle and gave rise to the deposition of the Burroughs beds. The sandstone at the base may be of either continental or marine origin, and no other continental deposits were formed. The sandy character of the limestone indicates equivocal conditions.

Macoupin cycle

Again only slightly changed conditions marked the beginning of the next cycle of deposition, the Macoupin. Conditions of stability and long weathering were reached later, however, as underclay, locally 6 feet thick, occurs in some places. These conditions prevailed until extensive swamps were formed. The peat of these swamps gave rise eventually to a coal bed which does not attain more than one foot in thickness. After the peat was formed, the sea presumably advanced rather suddenly, as thin-shelled marine organisms lie directly on the coal in some places. The deepening of the waters brought about the deposition of black platy shale in some places and a gray calcareous clay elsewhere. The seas gradually cleared and conditions extremely favorable to marine life were attained, for the Macoupin limestone carries abundant faunal remains, with fragments of corals, crinoids, and large spiriferoid brachiopods. Due either to the long time that had elapsed since the Burroughs limestone was deposited or to different environmental conditions, the Macoupin fauna was radically different from that in the Burroughs limy seas.

Conditions of marine deposition continued for a long time, as indicated by the thickness of the series of thin limestones and calcareous shales of late Macoupin age.

Shoal Creek cycle

Deposition continued from the Macoupin cycle with but slightly modified conditions. Only some scattered thin seams of coal were formed. Above the coal horizons numerous thin limestone bands were deposited, interbedded with carbonaceous and fossiliferous clays. Then shoaling of the waters developed another marshy land surface, marked by a humus horizon, above which a typical black platy shale was formed. The advancing sea in which this shale was deposited gradually deepened, and the Shoal Creek limestone was deposited.

McWain cycle

The close of Shoal Creek deposition was marked by deep channel cutting, which penetrated down into the Macoupin limestone. This is the last episode of Pennsylvanian history recorded in the area, but it does not record the close of the Pennsylvanian period. The entire McLeansboro group may have been deposited over the area and later removed. At the close of the Pennsylvanian period and in the following Permian period intense mountain-making movements of the earth's crust occurred in the Appalachians and elsewhere, even in the lower Mississippi Valley. Undoubtedly the Illinois basin experienced some uplift and warping at these times.

MESOZOIC AND CENOZOIC ERAS

The post-Pennsylvanian, pre-Pleistocene history of the Mississippi Valley region is a record of one or possibly two cycles of erosion.[11] The gravels left by some of the large and meandering streams were subsequently picked up by glacial ice, but some-

---

[11]Horberg, Leland, Preglacial erosion surfaces in Illinois: Jour. Geol., vol. 54, pp. 179-192, 1946. Reprinted as Illinois Geol. Survey Rept. Inv. 118. Horberg, Leland, Bedrock topography of Illinois: Illinois Geol. Survey Bull. 73, pp. 86-99, 1950.

times they escaped ice transportation.[12]
These gravels are characterized by an abundance of chert and small pebbles of vein
quartz. The chert pebbles usually are
heavily coated with iron stain, giving them
a "bronzed" appearance. The rounded,
whitish quartz pebbles are abundant in the
glacial deposits, and some of the flood-plain
gravels along Macoupin Creek contain
pebbles suggestive of the "bronzed" cherts.
Probably these are but scattered residues of
Tertiary gravels much reworked by ice and
water.

During the erosion cycle in the Cretaceous period, the sea invaded the Mississippi Valley from the south and west, and parts
of southern and possibly western Illinois
were inundated. With the uplift and
mountain-making that closed the Cretaceous
period in the West, the Mississippi Valley
was elevated somewhat, the sea excluded,
and a new erosion cycle began. This continued until shortly before the Pleistocene
period, when a second uplift rejuvenated the
streams again and renewed erosion, which
probably modified the surface of the Carlinville quadrangle.

Pleistocene Period

Following the uplift and the mountain
building that terminated the Pliocene, the
Pleistocene period, or age of continental
glaciation, set in. Ice sheets accumulated in
Labrador, in the region west of Hudson Bay
(Keewatin center), and in the Canadian
Rocky Mountains (Cordilleran center).
At least four major advances of the ice
from either or both the Labradorean and

Keewatin centers are recorded in the upper
Mississippi Valley. Estimates of students
in this field place the beginning of the
Pleistocene as one to two million years ago,[13]
an estimate of much interest because, during
or just before the beginning of the Ice Age,
man made his appearance on earth.

KANSAN AGE

The earliest advance of the ice recorded
in the quadrangle was the Kansan from the
Keewatin center. What may be Kansan
till has been discovered as far south as
Schuline in Randolph County.[14] The Kansan till possibly was not deposited in great
thickness over the Carlinville area, or it
has been largely removed by erosion. The
Kansan drift is generally calcareous but
thoroughly oxidized, and the horizons of
deep leaching and gumbotil, which charac-
terize the Kansan till elsewhere, are either
buried by the Illinoian till or have been removed by erosion.

YARMOUTH AGE

Following the disappearance of the Kansan glacier, the land remained in low and
poorly drained condition for probably the
longest of the interglacial intervals. From
the wood fragments sometimes appearing in
the Illinoian till and from the peat occasionally found in outcrops, it seems that the land
was well wooded during this interval and
that swamps existed. Both stream erosion
and stream aggradation are thought to have
been active because the Yarmouth fauna is
largely flood-plain land mollusks.

ILLINOIAN AGE

The Illinoian glacier came definitely from
the Labradorean center and advanced over
the quadrangle from the northeast, as is
indicated by striae on the bedrock in several
places and on till in one place (p. 47).
Illinoian deposits filled the pre-existing
valleys, and the valleys now existing were
re-excavated during and since the melting of
the Illinoian glacier.

[12]Cady, G. H., Geology and mineral resources of the Hennepin-La Salle quadrangle: Illinois Geol. Survey Bull. 37, pp. 69-70, 1919.
Thwaites, F. T., and Twenhofel, W. H., Windrow formation, an upland gravel formation of the driftless area and adjacent areas of the Upper Mississippi Valley: Geol. Soc. Amer. Bull., vol. 32, pp. 293-314, 1921.
Trowbridge, A. C., The erosional history of the drift-less area: Univ. of Iowa Studies in Nat. Hist., vol. 9, no. 3, 1921.
Udden, J. A., Geology and mineral resources of the Peoria quadrangle, Illinois: U. S. Geol. Survey Bull. 506, p. 50, 1912.
Rubey, W. W., Geology and mineral resources of the Hardin and Brussels quadrangles: U. S. Geol. Survey Prof. Paper 218, in press.
Lamar, J. E., and Sutton, A. H., Cretaceous and Tertiary sediments of Kentucky, Illinois, and Missouri: Amer. Assn. Petr. Geol. Bull., vol. 14, pp. 857-859, 1930.
Willman, H. B., and Payne, J. N., Geology and mineral resources of the Marseilles, Ottawa, and Streator quadrangles: Illinois Geol. Survey Bull. 66. pp. 140-141, 1942.
Horberg, Leland, op. cit. Also, Preglacial gravels in Henry county, Illinois: Illinois Acad. Sci. Trans., vol. 43, pp. 171-175, 1950.

[13]Willman, H. B., and Payne, J. Norman, Geology and mineral resources of the Marseilles, Ottawa, and Streator quadrangles: Illinois Geol. Survey Bull. 66, p. 209 and table 9, 1942.
[14]MacClintock, Paul, Correlation of the pre-Illinoian drifts of Illinois: Jour. Geol., vol. 41, p. 711, fig. 1, 1933.

Since Illinoian time all parts of the surface have been exposed to weathering and erosion except the low areas that stood under water. As the surface of the quadrangle, which is so relatively even, is developed on the Illinoian till and is not aggraded to any marked extent by loess, it is believed that the Illinoian glacier was "stagnant" before it melted.[15] Coops Mound is believed to be a crevasse-filling in the Illinoian glacier, probably while it was "stagnating."

The Jacksonville moraine in the northeastern part of the quadrangle marks the position where the front of the Illinoian glacier stood for some time after readvancing from a partial retreat, when the forward movement of the glacier was about balanced by the rate of the melting of the ice along its margin. While the ice stood at this position, the water derived from its melting flowed southwesterly and deposited outwash material over the surface of the quadrangle and along the stream courses. The lower course of Macoupin Creek was clogged with the finer material carried by these waters, and the remnants of those deposits not yet removed by the present stream comprise the loess-covered terraces east of Carlinville.

SANGAMON AGE

During the Sangamon age the surface of the Illinoian till was exposed to weathering, and gumbotil was formed on areas ineffectively drained. The runoff of rains started gullies and channels, some of the most active valley development following in general the courses of the larger preglacial valleys. Otter and Macoupin creeks began to re-excavate their valleys. Bear Creek and Lick Creek continued the courses predetermined in part possibly by the water that passed between the tongues of stagnant ice and the rock walls of the pre-Illinoian valleys. Macoupin valley was heavily aggraded by Sangamon silts: nearly five feet of sand and silt regarded as Sangamon lies in the base of the terrace crossed by State Highway No. 4 southeast of Carlinville.

---

[15]Flint, R. F., The stagnation and dissipation of the last ice sheet: Geog. Review, vol. 19, pp. 256-289, 1929. Flint, R. F., Glaciation in northwestern Illinois: Amer. Jour. Sci., vol. 21 pp. 422-440, 1931.

Peats and marls were formed in small lakes or ponds in the surface irregularities of the Jacksonville moraine. The original depressions were gradually filled by organic remains. Undrained depressions still exist, but some of them may be due to subsidence above mines.

The deep weathering of the Illinoian till indicates that the Sangamon age was long, but not, however, as long as the Yarmouth interglacial age.

WISCONSIN AGE

Concomitant with the very beginning of Wisconsin glaciation, wind deposition of the Farmdale loess proceeded on the uplands in the Carlinville area, particularly in the west part of the quadrangle. The Farmdale loess deposits on valley slopes may be due to undercutting by headward-working streams and slumping on the slopes.

Later, Peorian loess accumulated in the Carlinville quadrangle while glaciers of Wisconsin age occupied the upper Mississippi Valley. Its source was apparently the river bottoms west of the quadrangle, as the loess is generally thickest in the northwest part of the quadrangle, although it is ten feet thick in the south part of Carlinville and nearly as thick on the terraces in the valley of Macoupin Creek south and southeast of Carlinville. It covers the slopes of some of the valley walls and is thinly distributed over the prairie uplands, where in some exposures it has been thoroughly leached. It is not fossiliferous as it is in the counties farther north.

RECENT AGE

The geologic processes which have been active in the quadrangle since the glaciers melted from the mainland of North America include weathering (development of the soil profile), erosion, slope wash, and wind work. The growth of vegetation is a significant factor modifying the other processes. Erosion has developed to the point where possibly only one-fourth of the upland area is ineffectively drained. The larger streams, Otter and Macoupin creeks, have not only widened but deepened their valleys. Macoupin Creek has cut through Sangamon and Peorian silts to develop terraces. The larger tributaries — Massa, Lick, Bear, and Hurricane creeks — have extended their courses headward and have deepened their valleys slightly below the old bedrock surface. At flood times a good deal of alluvial material has been distributed along valley floors, aggrading the valley flats and covering the rock or till floors to a depth of fully seven feet.

Other material in present process of slow transportation is the thin mantle of material (slope wash) lying on the steep slopes of the valley walls, which, loosened by frost work every spring, moves downward and gradually becomes a part of the valley-bottom alluvium. Dust is blown from freshly plowed fields and newly laid alluvium, but the aggregate amount is too small to be noticeable. The constant mechanical and chemical work going on at and beneath the upland surface contributes to the soil growth. The changes induced by man, such as tiling the fields, diversion of drainage, and use of groundwater in wells, are contributing to the increase or decrease of energy in other geological activities. The sum total of all these processes is to reduce and level the land so that the sea may more easily invade the land.

CHAPTER VIII — ECONOMIC GEOLOGY

MINERAL RESOURCES

The mineral resources of the Carlinville quadrangle which have been or are being exploited include coal, limestone, shale and clay, groundwater, and soil. Gravel and sand is present only in negligible quantities, and the possibility that there is oil and gas in commercial quantities is small.

COAL

The Herrin (No. 6) coal is the only coal of current commercial importance in the quadrangle. Three other coals, the Sparland (No. 7), the Trivoli (No. 8), and the Macoupin (No. 9), which occur above the Herrin (No. 6) coal, are too thin to be of commercial importance. The No. 2 coal, which lies about 100 feet below the No. 6 coal, is reported to average about $3\frac{1}{3}$ feet in thickness and so has potential commercial value.

The Herrin (No. 6) coal, also known as the Belleville coal, was mined in the quadrangle at least as early as 1870, and by 1879 the three mines operating in Carlinville were producing annually an aggregate of more than 500,000 "bushels" of coal and employing more than fifty men. By 1910 some of the mines had been abandoned, and by 1924 all were shut down. Since then, mines in Virden and Carlinville (fig. 20) were operated occasionally for local supplies and have been operated practically continuously since 1930. The mine at Virden became a shipping mine in 1938, and between then and 1943 produced 667,613 tons of coal, or a little less than one-fourth of the coal produced in the county.[1]

The Herrin (No. 6) coal varies in thickness from 3 to 8 feet (pl. 4), the maximum thickness being reported in the Standard Oil Company's core-drill test three-fourths of a mile east of Schoper. Thicknesses of only 4 to 6 inches are known locally west

of Girard, but it is possible that the seam has been affected by erosion here and also in the southeastern part of the quadrangle where thicknesses of 4 to 6 feet are reported near the location of maximum thickness.[2,3] The coal has not been mined to any extent in the quadrangle where the thickness is less than 6 feet, and for this reason, and also because of the location of the railroads, mining has been restricted to the eastern part of the quadrangle.

The coal characteristically occurs in "benches" or layers, sometimes separated by partings or thin laminae of pyritic or shaly material or of fusain. Each bench is bright, banded coal composed mainly of vitrain and clarain with considerable fusain. The thickest bench is at the top of the bed, where the coal appears most compact because in general the banding is finer. A clay parting, the well-known "blue band," is a distinguishing characteristic of this coal and occurs usually between 1 and 2 feet above the base of the coal. It ranges from $\frac{3}{4}$ of an inch to 2 inches in thickness.

Proximate analyses of face samples indicate that the rank index of the coal mined in the quadrangle is between 119 and 123 and that the coal is therefore a high-volatile bituminous C coal.[4]

Mining conditions, especially the character of the roof rock, are not ideal, and may in large part account for the small amount of mining now being carried on in the quadrangle. Not uncommonly the shale lying between the coal and the limestone "caprock" becomes so thick and so soft that its support during mining and in the entries is difficult; in places the caprock is interbedded irregularly with shale, so that it is likely to fall in large slabs. Lenses or "rolls" of gray shale between the coal and the overlying black shale create insecure roof

---

[1]Coal Reports of Illinois, Department of Mines and Minerals, 1937-1943, with the exception of 1941, for which the average production of the other years is used.

[2]Lee, Wallace, U. S. Geol. Survey Atlas, Gillespie-Mount Olive folio (No. 220), p. 4, 1926.
[3]Kay, Fred H., Coal resources of District VII, Illinois Min. Inv. Coop. Bull. 11, p. 100, and plate 1, 1915.
[4]Cady. G. H., Classification and selection of Illinois coals: Illinois Geol. Survey Bulletin 62, 1935.

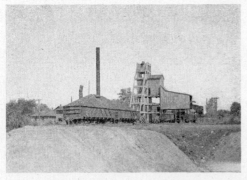 

FIG. 20.—Mine tipples in the Carlinville quadrangle. A. South mine, Carlinville, SW ¼ sec. 33, T. 10 N., R. 7 W. (Carlinville Twp.). B. Standard Oil Company Mine No. 1, Carlinville, NE ¼ sec. 21, T. 10 N., R. 7 W. (Carlinville Twp.).

conditions locally and may cause fractures in the overlying black shale and limestone that, besides making these rocks insecure, provide access for water from strata above. Occasionally "bosses" may protrude a foot or more below the general lower surface of the caprock and are nuisances, particularly when one happens to occur over a haulage-way.

In general the underclay does not create mining problems, although where it becomes wet, it may "squeeze" out into the mined-out portions.

Excluding T. 10 N., R. 8 W. (Bird Twp.), T. 11 N., R. 8 W. (South Palmyra Twp.), and T. 12 N., R. 7 W. (North Otter Twp.), because in them no drill tests have been made, and T. 12 N., R. 8 W. (North Palmyra Twp.), because there the coal seems to be too thin for commercial production, assuming an average thickness of 6 feet for the rest of the quadrangle, and deducting a mined-out area of approximately 10 square miles, the estimated reserves of coal No. 6 in the quadrangle are about 1,036,800,000 tons.

OIL AND GAS

The possibilities for the production of oil and gas are not considered promising, although the Carlinville gas and oil field that lies just south of the quadrangle supplied Carlinville with illuminating gas for several years[5] and by the end of 1914 had pro-

duced 16,540 barrels of oil.[6] Some oil and gas has been produced in the quadrangle from wells in what is now known as the Carlinville North pool,[7] in secs. 19 and 20, T. 10 N., R. 7 W., northwest of Carlinville. This field was opened in 1913-14, when one well is reported to have had an initial production of 100 barrels.[8] "At least one well was drilled in 1921. The recent drilling began late in 1941, and there were three producing and eight abandoned oil wells in July 1942."[7] A well southwest of Carlinville was yielding a small amount of gas in 1944.

The gas and oil are obtained from lenticular bodies of sand that lie near the base of the Pennsylvanian system about 220 feet below the Herrin (No. 6) coal and range from 2 to 70 feet and average about 40 feet in thickness. The most favorable places for oil accumulation seem to be on the slopes of low domes over which the sandstone lenses apparently do not extend but "wedge" out.[9] Favorable structures of this kind have not been mapped on the Carlinville quadrangle.

Consideration of other oil and gas possibilities in the quadrangle has been published by the Illinois State Geological Survey.[10]

[5]Kay, F. H., The Carlinville oil and gas field: Illinois Geol. Survey Bull. 20, Year-book for 1910, pp. 83-94, plates VIII-X, 1915.

[6]Lee, Wallace, U. S. Geol. Survey Atlas, Gillespie-Mount Olive folio (No. 220), p. 13, 1926.
[7]Easton, W. H., Oil and gas possibilities in Structure of Herrin (No. 6) coal bed in Macoupin County, etc.: Illinois Geol. Survey Circ. 88, p. 30, 1942.
[8]Blatchley, R. S., Oil and gas in Bond, Macoupin and Montgomery counties, Illinois: Illinois Geol. Survey Bull. 28, p. 11, 1914.
[9]Lee, Wallace, Oil and gas in Gillespie and Mount Olive quadrangles, oil investigations in Illinois in 1914: Illinois Geol. Survey Bull. 31, p. 98, fig. 20, 1915.
[10]Easton, op. cit., pp. 27-39.

As oil and gas generally occurs at the top of anticlines, only such structures as are revealed by the elevations of coal No. 6 (pl. 3) in the quadrangle are considered as possible sources. No structures other than those revealed by the coal bed are known in the older beds.

Anderson anticline. — This anticline has not been adequately tested, although several coal test borings have been made on it. The only test boring that penetrated nearly to the base of the Pennsylvanian system is in the SE ¼ NW ¼ sec. 12, T. 10 N., R. 7 W. (Carlinville Twp.), on the west side of the structure. It passed through both the "Carlinville" and "Litchfield" sands without any shows of oil. However, "drilling is not recommended because the structure has no closure,"[11] although a small low dome was once located in secs. 26 and 35, T. 11 N., R. 7 W. (South Otter Twp.).[12]

Burton anticline. — The Carlinville North pool is restricted to a local dome on the north side of the Burton anticline. Other test wells have been drilled on the anticline east of Carlinville. "Two wells in sec. 35 had gas shows, one . . . in shale and sandstone at 395-405 feet and the other . . . in shale at 407-413 feet. The well in sec. 24, T. 10 N., R. 7 W., had a possible show of gas below 547 feet and a very slight show of oil at 550 feet (total depth). Without known closure, further drilling along this anticline does not seem advisable."[13] However, it seems possible that a well in the city of Carlinville, drilled to a depth of 520 feet or more, might strike oil or gas in this structure. It is reported that traces of gas have been detected in wells drilled in the city, but none of these are deep enough to test the most likely producing horizons.

Carlinville anticline. — Only the northeast end of this structure lies in the quadrangle. Most of the oil and gas produced from the Carlinville pool south of the quadrangle came from local domes on this anticline. "The broad 'high' at the east end

of the Carlinville anticline in and about secs. 32 and 33, T. 10 N., R. 6 W. . . . has not been tested by any well reaching the lower Pennsylvanian. Doming or reversals of dip are not known but may occur. This is a possible producing area, but not enough data are available to suggest a location."[7]

Modesto anticline. — "There has been only one important well drilled on this anticline . . . in sec. 17, T. 12 N., R. 7 W. The well ended in the St. Louis limestone, topped at 563 feet, but no shows of oil or gas were reported. There is no present indication of closure on the anticline, hence prospecting is not recommended."[14]

Nilwood anticline. — Only one deep test, in sec. 9, T. 10 N., R. 6 W., has been drilled on the Nilwood anticline. It was completed in the St. Louis limestone at 695 feet. No shows of oil or gas were reported.

"To the east . . . two wells had shows of oil. One [is] in sec. 35, T. 11 N., R. 6 W., and the other, in sec. 2, T. 10 N., R. 6 W., produced a little oil but is temporarily abandoned.

"There is no known reversal of dip on the Nilwood anticline, but additional data may prove the presence of one or more domes. The presence of anticlinal noses along the east margin of the structure might be an indication of the presence of domes updip. Recommendations for drilling can not be made."[15]

SHALE AND CLAY

The Carlinville quadrangle contains a variety of clays and shales of the kind found in other parts of Illinois.

INDUSTRY

The only clay products plant operated recently in the Carlinville quadrangle is that of Moody Co. (fig. 21), located in the NE ¼ SE ¼ sec. 32, T. 10 N., R. 7 W. (Carlinville Twp.), at the south edge of Carlinville where the clay deposit described below was exposed.

[11]Easton, *op. cit.*, p. 29.
[12]Rich, John, Structure map of the Herrin coal, Carlinville quadrangle, unpublished map.
[13]Easton, *op. cit.*, pp. 29-30.
[14]Easton, *op. cit.*, pp. 32-33.
[15]Easton, *op. cit.*, p. 33.

Section of Clay in Moody Co. Pit

		Ft.
4	Clay, silty, brown (sample NF-110)	2½
3	Clay, silty, brown; more clayey than overlying bed	1
2	Silt, clayey, gray; contains a few small chert pebbles . .	Sample NF-111 2
1	Clay, silty, dark brown; contains small black pellets . .	½

The exposed clay and about an additional three feet of clay below is noncalcareous, as a result of weathering, which is also believed to account for some of the differences in the materials exposed in the pit. The clay-mineral material in the clays is illite.

The uppermost clay bed was used for the production of sand-mold brick, and the bottom three layers are mixed for making common brick, drain tile, and building block. Three round down-draft kilns were used for burning.

Results of ceramic tests on the two samples from Moody Co. pit are given in table 10.

The Carlinville Tile Company plant and pit are located in the NW ¼ NE ¼ SW ¼ sec. 33, T. 10 N., R. 7 W. (Carlinville Twp.), at the south outskirts of Carlinville. Shale from the upper part of the Carlinville

cyclothem and the overlying glacial drift were mixed and used for making brick, drain tile, and hollow block and tile. The plant had not been operated for some time, and the clay materials in the pit were slumped so badly that an adequate examination of them could not be made.

RESOURCES

The clay resources of the Carlinville quadrangle consist of bedrock shales and clays, glacial till, and loess.

Bedrock shale. — Several shale formations in the Carlinville quadrangle locally have thicknesses of 10 feet or more, but the Carlinville ·and the Trivoli shales are generally the thickest and most available. The Carlinville shale is about 15 feet thick in the south part of the quadrangle and along Macoupin Creek (geologic sections 14 and 15, Appendix A). Ceramic tests on a sample of this shale (NF-117), taken from an 11-foot exposure along Macoupin Creek in the NW ¼ sec. 35, T. 10 N., R. 7 W. (Carlinville Twp.) (geologic section 15), indicate that it has possibilities for the manufacture of common and face brick, paving brick, drain tile, quarry tile, roofing tile, structural tile, and sewer pipe.

Fig. 21.—Clay pit of Moody Company.

TABLE 10.—CERAMIC TESTS REPORTED BY C. W. PARMELEE, DEPARTMENT OF CERAMIC ENGINEERING, UNIVERSITY OF ILLINOIS

SAMPLE NO. NF-104

Formation: Macoupin cyclothem.
Locality: NW ¼ NE ¼ NW ¼ sec. 2, T. 9 N., R. 7 W. (Brushy Mound Twp.) (geologic section 19).
Kind of Material: Clay.
Reaction for Carbonates: Positive.
Color: Medium gray with occasional brownish iron staining. Limestone pebbles may be noted.
Hardness: Medium. Granular fracture.
Working Property: Quickly wedged, very slightly sticky.
Water of Plasticity: 33.9%

TRANSVERSE STRENGTH TESTS OF UNBURNED CLAY WITH 50% STANDARD SAND

Number of Briq.: 12   Modulus of Rupture; Lbs. Per Sq. In.: 260

FINENESS

Percent of Residue: Character of Residue:
35 mesh   Chiefly two large calcite
8.32%   pebbles (½″ diam.). Surfaces of pebbles show pyrite.

DRYING

Air Shrinkage: Linear 12.7%; volume 43.1%
Drying Conduct: Scum, otherwise satisfactory.
Scumming: Very bad.

BURNING TEST

Cone	Porosity, percent	Color	Hardness	Burning shrinkage Lin.—Vol.		Total shrinkage Lin.—Vol.	
06	19.9	Pale salmon.............	5	3.2	9.4	15.9	52.5
03	17.6	Salmon.................	6	3.2	9.4	15.9	52.5
01	11.5	Salmon.................	7	4.8	13.6	17.5	56.7
2	1.8	Light chocolate.........	8	5.9	16.8	18.6	59.9
3+	0.6	Medium chocolate.......	8	6.7	18.8	19.4	61.9
6—ᵃ	4.0	Chocolate..............	8	−0.4	−1.3	12.3	41.8

ᵃBloated, cracked, and sticky.

Suggested Uses: The presence of calcite as pebbles is objectionable. This fault and the bad scumming will limit the use of this clay to common brick.

SAMPLE NO. NF-106

Formation: Shoal Creek cyclothem.
Locality: SW ¼ SW ¼ SE ¼ sec. 35, T. 10 N., R. 7 W. (Carlinville Twp.) (geologic section 19).
Kind of Material: Clay.
Reaction for Carbonates: Positive.
Color: Medium dark gray; occasional brownish iron stain.
Hardness: Fairly hard for a clay. Shows slickensides.
Working Property: Works easily. Very slightly sticky.

FINENESS

Percent of Residue: Character of Residue:
35 mesh   Calcite pebble. Very small
0.22%   pyrite grains.

DRYING

Air Shrinkage: Linear 28.6%; volume 65.9%.
Drying Conduct: Cracks in drying.
Scumming: Marked.

BURNING TEST

Cone	Porosity, percent	Color	Hardness	Burning shrinkage Lin.—Vol.		Total shrinkage Lin.—Vol.	
06	5.2	Pale orange............	6				
02ᵃ	0.5	Light brown...........	7				
4—ᵇ	16.0	Tan.................	7				

ᵃBadly cracked, oxidized, reduced and reoxidized.
ᵇBloated and cracked.

Suggested Uses: This material has serious defects which will probably prevent its use: the presence of the limestone pebbles and pyrite, excessive drying shrinkage, cracking during drying, scumming, cracking during burning.

SAMPLE NO. NF-108

Formation: Macoupin cyclothem.
Locality: NW ¼ SE ¼ sec. 25, T. 10 N., R. 7 W.
(Carlinville Twp.) (geologic section 29).
Kind of Material: Shale.
Reaction for Carbonates: Negative.
Color: Tan, with brownish iron stains along laminations. Sample also includes a few percent of a dark gray shale in small pieces.

Hardness: Typical. Laminated fracture.
Working Property: Works nicely. Not sticky. Some tendency to tear in cutting.

DRYING

Air Shrinkage: Linear 7.5%; volume 24.2%.
Drying Conduct: Satisfactory.
Scumming: Very slight.

BURNING TEST

Cone	Porosity, percent	Color	Hardness	Burning shrinkage Lin.—Vol.	Total shrinkage Lin.—Vol.
06	10.7	Salmon.................	4–5		
02[a]	0.1	Red...................	6		
4[b]	0.3	Maróon...............	8		

[a]Vitreous fracture.
[b]Black cored from reduction after original oxidation. Not visibly overfired.

Suggested Uses: Face brick, common brick, drain tile, structural tile, and roofing tile.

SAMPLE NO. NF-110

Formation: Peorian loess.
Locality: Moody Co. pit, NE ¼ SE ¼ sec. 32, T. 10 N., R. 7 W. (Carlinville Twp.) (geologic section 54) (fig. 21). Upper 30 inches of exposure.
Kind of Material: Clay.
Reaction for Carbonates: Negative.
Color: Yellow, occasional lumps show dark specks.
Hardness: Soft. Granular fracture.
Working Property: Wedges easily, slightly sticky.
Water of Plasticity: 34.9%

TRANSVERSE STRENGTH TESTS OF UNBURNED CLAY WITH 50% STANDARD SAND

Number of Briq.: 11 Modulus of Rupture: Lbs. Per Sq. In.: 349

FINENESS

Percent of Residue: 35 mesh 2.20% Character of Residue: Limonite pebbles, ⅛" and smaller.

DRYING

Air Shrinkage: Volume 39.4%.
Drying Conduct: Satisfactory.
Scumming: None.

BURNING TEST

Cone	Porosity, percent	Color	Hardness	Burning shrinkage Lin.	Burning shrinkage Vol.	Total shrinkage Lin.	Total shrinkage Vol.
06	28.9	Salmon.................	2–3	0.6	1.8	12.3	41.2
03	24.8	Red...................	4–5	2.6	7.6	14.3	47.0
01	17.1	Red...................	6	5.2	14.8	16.9	54.2
2	16.0	Red...................	7	5.6	15.8	17.3	55.2
4[a]	12.7	Red...................	8	6.2	17.4	17.9	56.8
6–	7.5	Maroon................	8	7.3	20.2	19.0	59.6
8[b]	4.2	Deep maroon...........	8	4.2	12.2	15.9	51.6

[a]No evidence of reduction, probably reoxidized.
[b]Sticky.

Suggested Uses: This clay is readily workable but slightly sticky. It contains limonite pebbles or granules which may cause specks. The drying conduct is satisfactory. The burning conduct is satisfactory, and the fine red color and uniformity of shade over a wide temperature range are notable. Suggested uses are for common and face brick, structural tile, and drain tile.

SAMPLE NO. NF-111

Formation: Peorian loess.
Locality: Moody Co. pit, NE ¼ SE ¼ sec. 32, T. 10 N., R. 7 W. (Carlinville Twp.) (geological section 54) (fig. 21). Lower 40 inches of exposure.
Kind of Material: Clay.
Reaction for Carbonates: Negative.
Color: Yellow, rather uniform.
Hardness: Soft. Finely granular fracture.
Working Property: Works nicely. Not sticky but difficult to slick with spatula.
Water of Plasticity: 27.4%

TRANSVERSE STRENGTH TESTS OF UNBURNED CLAY WITH 50% STANDARD SAND

Number of Briq.: 14   Modulus of Rupture; Lbs. Per Sq. In.: 480

FINENESS

Percent of Residue: Character of Residue:
35 mesh   Limonite and quartz
1.12%   grains.

DRYING

Air Shrinkage: Linear 8.4%; volume 27.5%.
Drying Conduct: Satisfactory.
Scumming: None.

BURNING TEST

Cone	Porosity, percent	Color	Hardness	Burning shrinkage Lin.—Vol.		Total shrinkage Lin.—Vol.	
06	28.4	Salmon	3	−0.3	−0.8	8.1	26.7
03	25.7	Light red	6	1.4	4.1	9.8	31.6
01	17.4	Red	6–7	4.2	12.0	12.6	39.5
3−	11.6	Maroon	8	5.9	16.6	14.3	44.1
3+[a]	11.4	Maroon	8	6.0	16.8	14.4	44.3
6−	1.6	Deep maroon	8	6.9	19.3	15.3	46.8
8[b]	11.4	Red-black	8	0.9	2.8	9.3	30.3

[a]Reoxidized from reduction in firing.
[b]Sticky and bloated.

Suggested Uses: This clay works well but not entirely smoothly when struck with a spatula. It may give trouble in flowing through a die. The presence of limonite grains may cause specking. The drying conduct is satisfactory. It burns very well, giving good shades of red and a good range of color uniformity. The vitrifying conduct is good. Suggested uses are common and face brick, roofing tile, quarry tile, drain tile, and structural tile.

SAMPLE NO. NF-112

Formation: Trivoli cyclothem.
Locality: SE ¼ NE ¼ SW ¼ sec. 21, T. 10 N., R. 8 W. (Bird Twp.) (geologic section 2)
Kind of Material: Shale.
Reaction for Carbonates: Negative.
Color: Tan. Some brown iron staining along cleavages.

Hardness: Typical. Fracture laminated.
Working Property: Works nicely although slightly short.

DRYING

Air Shrinkage: Linear 5.9%; volume 18.9%.
Drying Conduct: Satisfactory.
Scumming: Trace.

BURNING TEST

Cone	Porosity, percent	Color	Hardness	Burning shrinkage Lin.—Vol.		Total shrinkage Lin.—Vol.	
06	13.5	Light red	3				
02	3.6	Red	6				
4[a]	0.2	Maroon	8				

[a]Slight black-coring from reduction after previous oxidation. Not overfired.

Suggested Uses: Face and common brick.

SAMPLE NO. NF-115

Formation: Trivoli cyclothem.
Locality: NE ¼ SW ¼ sec. 10, T. 11 N., R. 8 W.
(South Palmyra Twp.) (geologic section 3)
Kind of Material: Shale.
Reaction for Carbonates: Negative.
Color: Light gray. Brown surface discoloration gives whole a tan cast.
Hardness: Typical. Laminated fracture.
Working Property: Slightly slow wedging, not sticky but soft to handle.
Water of Plasticity: 29.1%

TRANSVERSE STRENGTH TESTS OF UNBURNED CLAY
WITH 50% STANDARD SAND

Number of Briq.: 13   Modulus of Rupture; Lbs.
                        Per Sq. In.: 162

DRYING

Air Shrinkage: Linear 6.6%; volume 21.0.
Drying Conduct: Satisfactory.
Scumming: Trace.

BURNING TEST

Cone	Porosity, percent	Color	Hardness	Burning shrinkage		Total shrinkage	
				Lin.—Vol.		Lin.—Vol.	
06	23.7	Light red.............	3	4.2	12.0	10.8	33.0
03[a]	6.5	Red...................	6	9.4	25.7	16.0	46.7
01	0.4	Red...................	6–7	11.1	29.8	17.7	50.8
3—	0.2	Maroon...............	8	11.3	30.3	17.9	51.3
3+[b]	0.0	Maroon...............	8	10.7	28.7	17.3	49.9
6—	0.1	Maroon...............	8	10.8	29.0	17.4	50.0
8[c]	9.9	Brown................	8	3.2	9.3	9.8	30.3

[a]Slight black core from reduction in firing, previously oxidized.
[b]Slight black core from reduction in firing, previously oxidized.
[c]Bloated and sticky.

Suggested Uses: The working properties are fair. The dry strength is sufficient but below average. The drying conduct and shrinkage are satisfactory. Scumming is present in a small degree. The burning conduct is notably good since there is an exceptionally long range of practically zero porosity. The colors when burned are good, and the range of good color is long. The suggested uses are common and face brick, roofing tile, quarry tile, drain tile, and structural tile.

SAMPLE NO. NF-117

Formation: Carlinville cyclothem.
Locality: W ½ NE ¼ NW ¼ sec. 35, T. 10 N.,
R. 7 W. (Carlinville Twp.) (geologic section 15)
Kind of Material: Shale.
Reaction for Carbonates: Negative.
Color: Light gray. Uniform.
Hardness: Typical. Laminated fracture.
Working Property: Works easily. Soft, not sticky.
Water of Plasticity: 30.3%.

TRANSVERSE STRENGTH TESTS OF UNBURNED CLAY
WITH 50% STANDARD SAND

Number of Briq.: 14   Modulus of Rupture; Lbs.
                        Per Sq. In.: 198

DRYING

Air Shrinkage: Linear 7.3%; volume 23.6%.
Drying Conduct: Satisfactory.
Scumming: Trace.

BURNING TEST

Cone	Porosity, percent	Color	Hardness	Burning shrinkage		Total shrinkage	
				Lin.—Vol.		Lin.—Vol.	
06	21.3	Salmon................	4	4.9	13.9	12.2	37.5
03[a]	1.5	Red...................	4–5	10.8	29.1	18.1	52.7
01	0.0	Dark red..............	6	11.0	29.6	18.3	53.2
2	0.1	Maroon................	7	11.3	30.3	18.6	53.9
4[b]	0.1	Deep maroon..........	8	10.3	27.7	17.6	51.3
6—[c]	0.0	Brown.................	8	10.9	29.3	18.2	52.9
8[d]	4.1	Green.................	7	0.5	1.4	7.8	25.0

[a]Black cored from reduction in firing.
[b]Black cored from reduction in firing, previously oxidized.
[c]Slightly sticky.
[d]Bloated and sticky.

Suggested Uses: This shale is readily brought to a good working consistency. It dries satisfactorily with a medium strength and without scumming. The burning conduct is very satisfactory since the material attains practically zero porosity at cone 01 and does not overburn until cone 6 is reached. Therefore, this material should be valuable for vitrified wares. The colors and color range are excellent. Suggested uses are common and face brick, paving brick, drain tile, sewer pipe, quarry tile, roofing tile, and structural tile.

Shales belonging to the Scottville, Trivoli, and Carlinville cyclothems crop out in considerable thicknesses along Bear and Massa creeks and their tributaries in the west part of the quadrangle (plate 1; geologic sections 1-7, 9, 16). The shales are generally more or less sandy and micaceous. Ceramic tests on a sample (table 10, NF-112), taken from about the middle 8 feet of Trivoli shale exposed in the south bank of Bear Creek in the SE ¼ NE ¼ SW ¼ sec. 21, T. 10 N., R. 8 W. (Bird Twp.) (geologic section 2), show that it has possibilities for face and common brick, and the tests on another sample (NF-115) of the Trivoli shale, taken from an exposure in the NE ¼ SW ¼ sec. 10, T. 11 N., R. 8 W. (South Palmyra Twp.) (geologic section 3), show that it has possibilities for common and face brick, quarry tile, drain tile, and structural tile.

In places the shale overlying the Macoupin limestone becomes fairly thick, and tests on a sample (NF-108), taken from the shale exposed along Macoupin Creek in the NW ¼ SE ¼ sec. 25, T. 10 N., R. 7 W. (Carlinville Twp.) (geologic section 29), show it to have possibilities for face brick, common brick, drain tile, structural tile, and roofing tile.

Bedrock clay. — The bedrock clays of the Carlinville quadrangle are underclays, that is, they lie below a coal or, when the coal is absent, below the horizon of the coal. Most of these underclays are comparatively thin, and they are limy except possibly for a few inches at the top. They are often popularly but erroneously called "fireclays." Fireclays are refractory, and although refractory clays do occur in the Pennsylvanian system, they are largely restricted to strata much older than the formations exposed in the Carlinville quadrangle. The tests on actual samples (table 10, NF-104 and NF-106) also indicate that none of the underclays of the Carlinville quadrangle are fireclays, although possibly where leached and highly weathered they might have properties approaching those of fireclays.

One of the thicker underclays in the quadrangle is that lying below the Macoupin coal. Tests on a sample (NF-104) of this underclay in an outcrop along a creek in the NW ¼ NE ¼ NW ¼ sec. 2, T. 9 N., R. 7 W. (Brushy Mound Twp.) (geologic section 19) show it to have possibilities for common brick.

Tests on a sample (NF-106) of the underclay of the Shoal Creek cyclothem, exposed in the SW ¼ SW ¼ SE ¼ sec. 35, T. 10 N., R. 7 W. (Carlinville Twp.) (geologic section 19), indicate that it has little value for the manufacture of ceramic products.

Glacial till. — Glacial till, a pebbly, bouldery clay, is widespread in the Carlinville quadrangle and underlies the loess and soil over large areas. Most of the till is calcareous, but thicknesses of 4 to 5 feet of noncalcareous pre-Illinoian till have been noted and the upper part of the Illinoian till is locally leached to a depth of 2 to 10 feet.

Till, calcareous as well as noncalcareous, is used for the manufacture of clay products where other kinds of clay and shale are not available, but it requires special treatment for the removal of pebbles, and if calcareous, burning it to a good color is often difficult. For these reasons shales or other materials, if available, are used in preference to till. Although no samples were tested, much of the till in the Carlinville quadrangle, especially the noncalcareous till, probably could be used for making common brick, drain tile, and possibly fireproofing, but the products might not equal in quality those which might be made from some of the shales or other clays that crop out in the quadrangle.

Loess. — Loess, a buff to light grayish-yellow, very silty clay or clayey silt, generally free from pebbles though in places it contains a few small chert pebbles, is widespread in the Carlinville quadrangle and underlies the soil of most of the uplands (pp. 52-53). It is of two different ages, of which the Peorian or younger is the more important because it is at or near the surface throughout much of the quadrangle. Where fresh it is calcareous, but in places, as at Moody Co. pit, it is weathered and noncalcareous to a depth of about 10 feet. The older Sangamon loess below the Peorian loess is noncalcareous and where readily available may be of equal potential value.

TABLE 11.—PHYSICAL TESTS ON LIMESTONES OF THE CARLINVILLE QUADRANGLE[a]

Sample No.	Formation	Specific gravity	Absorption (percent)	Wear (percent)
167[b]	Shoal Creek..........................	2.69	0.4	3.6
194[c]	Shoal Creek..........................	2.61	1.9	4.1
193[d]	Carlinville..........................	2.67	1.0	3.3

[a]Test made by State Highway Testing Laboratory, Illinois Division of Highways, Springfield, 1930.
[b]Same as NF-116, table 12.
[c]Same as NF-100, table 12.
[d]In SE ¼ NE ¼ sec. 34, T. 12 N., R. 8 W., 2 feet 6 inches thick.

Tests on the samples NF-110 and NF-111 (table 10) from the pit of Moody Co. show the ceramic characters of the Peorian loess. Both show that it has possibilities for the manufacture of common and face brick, structural tile, drain tile, and NF-111 indicates possibilities also for roofing tile and quarry tile.

Availability. — Samples of the clays and shales of the Carlinville quadrangle were collected where natural or artificial exposures afforded opportunity, and therefore the deposits sampled are not necessarily those most suitable for commercial exploitation. There are probably a number of upland areas adjacent to the several railroads which traverse the quadrangle where sufficient noncalcareous loess is present to support a clay-products plant of moderate size and where equally adequate deposits of noncalcareous till would probably be revealed by prospecting. Outcrops of the bedrock clays and shales, however, occur chiefly along the lower parts of the valley walls of the larger streams, where the overburden is usually heavy and consists not only of loess and till but also in many places of bedrock materials as well. The location of deposits of such bedrock clay or shale suitable for commercial development from the standpoint of availability will involve careful search and prospecting.

LIMESTONE

The limestones in the Carlinville quadrangle are generally less than 10 feet thick, and no deposits appear to be suitable for large-scale commercial operation. Outcrops occur primarily in the beds or valley walls of the streams of the area, and although there are small areas where the overburden is thin, there is usually a thick overburden consisting of both bedrock and glacial drift. There probably are upland areas where limestone lies immediately below glacial drift, but careful prospecting will be needed to locate and explore them. It is doubtful whether any of the limestones of the quadrangle are thick enough to make subsurface mining feasible.

It appears therefore that the limestone deposits of the quadrangle are of possible importance chiefly as sources of comparatively small quantities of agricultural limestone, roadstone, and concrete aggregate obtained by quarrying the stone readily available under thin overburden at natural outcrops.

The most important limestones in the quadrangle are the Shoal Creek, Carlinville, and Macoupin limestones. Samples were collected from six of the better outcrops.

The value of limestone for agricultural limestone is measured, so far as chemical composition is concerned, in terms of the Calcium Carbonate Equivalent. Most limestones sold commercially test over 90 percent C.C.E., but limestones having 75 to 90 percent C.C.E. are used in some places. According to the results of chemical analyses (table 12) the Shoal Creek and Carlinville limestones may be expected to have C.C.E.'s of about 90 percent or more.

The results of physical tests (table 11) suggest that many deposits of the Shoal Creek and Carlinville limestones may be suitable for concrete aggregate. The Macoupin and Burroughs limestones were not tested, but they are so impure that they are probably not suitable for concrete aggregate.

TABLE 12.—CHEMICAL ANALYSES[a] OF LIMESTONES IN THE CARLINVILLE QUADRANGLE

Sample No.	T.	R.	sec.	¼	¼	¼	Near	Formation	Thickness Ft.	Thickness In.	C.C.E.[f]
NF-100	10 N	7 W	36	Center		NW	Carlinville	Shoal Creek limestone[b]	6	0	92
NF-101	10 N	7 W	36	Center		NW	Carlinville	Shoal Creek limestone and shale[c]	3	0	69
NF-102	10 N	7 W	36	Center		NW	Carlinville	Shoal Creek limestone[d]	3	9	83
NF-103	9 N	7 W	2	NW	NE	NE	Carlinville	Burroughs limestone	3	0	63
NF-107	10 N	7 W	35	SE	NW	NE	Carlinville	Macoupin limestone	2	6	82
NF-109	10 N	7 W	30	NW	SE	NW	Carlinville	Carlinville limestone	4	7	93
NF-114	11 N	8 W	10		SW	SW	Palmyra	Carlinville limestone	3	7	87
NF-116	11 N	7 W	16		NW	NE	Nilwood	Shoal Creek limestone	3	6	97
R-2531	10 N	7 W	33			SW	Carlinville	Carlinville limestone	5	0	g90

Sample No.	SiO₂	Al₂O₃	Fe₂O₃	MnO	MgO	CaO	H₂O—	Loss on ignition	CaCO₃[e]	MgCO₃[e]
NF-100	5.57	1.81	1.77		1.49	49.72	0.26	40.16	88.73	3.12
NF-101	9.84		6.49	0.11	1.81	36.40		30.94	64.96	3.79
NF-102	25.47		11.02	0.25	3.08	43.10		36.90	76.92	6.44
NF-103	5.40		10.11	1.20	2.08	32.93		28.46	58.77	4.35
NF-107	2.13		3.07		3.05	42.56		37.29	75.95	6.38
NF-109	5.48	0.83	6.70	0.20	2.69	49.17	0.16	41.79	87.75	5.63
NF-114					3.53	44.76		39.33	79.88	7.38
NF-116					1.17	52.78		42.99	94.19	2.45
R-2531										

a Made by Geochemical Section, Illinois State Geological Survey.
b Items 16 and 17, geologic section 35.
c Items 13-15, geologic section 35.
d Items 11 and 12, geologic section 35.
e Obtained from CaO and MgO by factorial multiplication.
f Calcium carbonate equivalent. This figure is the sum of the calculated CaCO₃ and MgCO₃. Calcium carbonate equivalent is usually determined by a direct measurement, but the figure here given is thought to be close to the values which would be obtained in that way.
g Determined directly.

Fɪɢ. 22.—Shoal Creek limestone in old quarry in the NW ¼ sec. 36, T. 10 N., R. 7 W. (Carlinville Twp.) (geologic section 35).

Small amounts of native limestone have been used for bridge and wall foundations and for walling and curbing wells. Probably local limestones might be used more for building stone, but only those limestones which show satisfactory weather resistance in natural outcrops should be used.

Shoal Creek limestone.—This limestone was sampled at two places, one in the center of the NW ¼ sec. 36, T. 10 N., R. 7 W. (Carlinville Twp.) (geologic section 35, fig. 22) and the other along a tributary to East Fork Otter Creek in the NE ¼ NW ¼ NE ¼ sec. 16, T. 11 N., R. 7 W. (South Otter Twp.) (geologic section 36).

Results of chemical analyses on samples from the first locality are given in table 12, samples NF-100, NF-101 and NF-102, and of physical tests in table 11, sample 194. Together the samples represent a thickness of almost 10 feet of limestone. Other small outcrops of the same limestone stratum occur downstream from the outcrop sampled.

At the other locality a 3½-foot limestone is exposed in the bed of the stream for a distance of about 250 feet. Tests on samples from this deposit are given in tables 11 and 12, samples 167 and NF-116.

Carlinville limestone.—Chemical analyses were made of two samples of this limestone (table 12). Sample NF-109 was taken from 4'7" of the limestone exposed in the valley flat of Hurricane Creek in the NW ¼ SE ¼ SE ¼ sec. 30, T. 10 N., R. 7 W. (Carlinville Twp.) (geologic section 10). Sample NF-114 represents 3 feet 7 inches of limestone visible in a small creek in the SW ¼ NW ¼ sec. 10, T. 11 N., R. 8 W. (S. Palmyra Twp.) (geologic section 9). Physical tests were made on sample 193 taken from 2½ feet of limestone in the SE ¼ NE ¼ sec. 34, T. 12 N., R. 8 W. (N. Palmyra Twp.) (geologic section 8). This limestone crops out at intervals for half a mile along both sides of a tributary to Massa Creek. It has been considerably used locally for bridge abutments, foundations, and similar purposes.

Macoupin limestone.—One of the best exposures of the Macoupin limestone in the Carlinville quadrangle occurs along Macoupin Creek in the SE ¼ NW ¼ NE ¼ sec. 35, T. 10 N., R. 7 W. (Carlinville Twp.) (geologic section 26). Sample NF-107, table 12, was taken from the outcrop.

Burroughs limestone.—This limestone crops out at a number of places in the quadrangle and was sampled from a three-foot exposure in a gully in NW ¼ NE ¼ NW ¼ sec. 2, T. 9 N., R. 7 W. (Brushy Mound Twp.) (geologic section 19), sample NF-103. A chemical analysis of the sample is given in table 12.

SAND AND GRAVEL

The most obvious sources of sand and gravel in the Carlinville quadrangle are the alluvial deposits in the valley flats of some of the major streams, especially the lower course of Bear Creek in T. 10 N., R. 8 W. (Bird Twp.), Anderson and Richardson creeks in the northeast part of T. 10 N., R. 7 W. (Carlinville Twp.), and Macoupin Creek. Probably not much gravel could be obtained at any one place because these deposits are usually thin, but by working along the stream valleys it is possible that in places gravel could be obtained in sufficient amounts and of satisfactory character for surfacing short stretches of roads. The

deposits have been derived principally from glacial outwash and from the glacial drift and bedrock exposed along the stream valleys; and because the bedrock includes considerable amounts of shale, it is likely that the shale content of the deposits usually will be too high for their use in concrete aggregate and mortar (table 13).

Besides the alluvial sands and gravels, pockets of sand and gravel occur within the glacial drift, and along Macoupin Creek there are terrace areas of sand and gravel covered by loess. Possibly some of the deposits in the drift might yield small quantities of material. Little is known regarding the character of the terrace deposits, and they may be worthy of exploration as a possible source of considerable amounts of gravel. Some of them are tracts 30 or 40 acres in area.

SANDSTONE

The only sandstone exposed to any extent in the quadrangle is the McWain sandstone where it crops out at the mouth of a

TABLE 13.—MECHANICAL ANALYSIS AND PEBBLE COUNT[a] OF SAMPLE NF-113, TAKEN FROM A 2-FOOT EXPOSURE OF GRAVEL IN THE BED OF BEAR CREEK IN THE SW ¼ SEC. 21, T. 10 N., R. 8 W. (BIRD TWP.)

Sieve	Percent retained	Sieve	Percent retained
1 inch	0.7	35 mesh	14.3
¾ inch	0.2	48 mesh	18.5
½ inch	0.6	65 mesh	6.4
⅜ inch	1.7	100 mesh	2.0
4 mesh	8.3	150 mesh	0.3
6 mesh	6.2	200 mesh	0.1
10 mesh	14.8	270 mesh	Trace
20 mesh	14.2	Pan	0.7
28 mesh	9.7	Clay	1.3
		Total	100.0

Kind of rock	Percent by number of pebbles	Kind of rock	Percent by number of pebbles
Limestone	10	Chert	33
Dolomite	6	Granite	1
Sandstone, ferruginous	24	Other igneous rocks	1
Shale	10	Metamorphic rock	1
Ferruginous concretions	1	Altered dolerite	6
Quartz	7	Total	100

[a]Pebble count of pebbles ¼ to ½ inch in size. The number of pebbles larger than ½ inch was too small to permit a representative count.

tributary gully to Macoupin Creek in the SE ¼ sec. 25, T. 10 N., R. 7 W. (Carlinville Twp.) (geologic section 33). Although the sandstone extends along the south and east valley wall of the creek for some rods, only a comparatively small quantity is readily available under thin overburden.

PEAT

Peat is exposed at two places in the quadrangle, namely in the SE ¼ sec. 10, T. 11 N., R. 7 W. (South Otter Twp.) (geologic section 46), and in the SE ¼ sec. 3, T. 11 N., R. 8 W. (South Palmyra Twp.) (geologic section 45). The peat is so thin and the overburden is so heavy at both localities that it is doubtful if the peat is commercially important, but small amounts might be secured for limited uses.

GROUNDWATER GEOLOGY

The glacial drift and the upper Pennsylvanian strata are the geologic sources of groundwater in the Carlinville quadrangle. No deep wells have been drilled for water in the pre-Pennsylvanian strata.

The large-diameter dug wells derive their supplies from the saturated zone just below the water table, generally from fine drift materials of low permeability. A few wells encounter shallow sand deposits of greater permeability.

Drilled wells in the drift deposits derive their supplies from sands and gravels whose water is generally under some artesian pressure. In general these wells are deeper than the dug wells, and often penetrate to the top of the bedrock. The areas in the quadrangle most promising for future development of water supplies from the glacial drift are along the preglacial valleys (pl. 1). The northeast-to-southwest valley and its tributaries, in the north half of the quadrangle, and the east-to-west valley and its tributaries, across the south half of the quadrangle, were the main channels by which water from the melting glaciers crossed the area. The large volumes of meltwater in these valleys tended to sort the debris from the glaciers, carrying the finer materials

away and leaving the coarser materials, so that the cleanest and best-sorted deposits of sand and gravel in the area would be expected to occur along these valleys.

Some of the upper Pennsylvanian strata in this area, usually the thin sandstones, are water-bearing. These sandstones are normally very fine in texture, are partially cemented, and have low porosities and permeabilities that greatly limit the amount of water that can move through them. In general the water from the Pennsylvanian rocks is more highly mineralized than that contained in the drift deposits.

Prospecting tests along Macoupin Creek by the City of Carlinville water works in 1934 revealed water-bearing sands and gravels at depths of 18 to 26 feet and penetrated Pennsylvanian strata for short distances, in one instance finding salt water in what is possibly the Trivoli cyclothem. On the uplands in Carlinville the Starr Brothers Creamery well for cooling water is 330 feet deep and extends into the Carbondale group below the Herrin (No. 6) coal. A well at the cemetery east of town, reported by Mr. Mayfield, was drilled 110 feet from the bottom of an 18-foot dug well but failed to yield water; it extended to either the Carlinville or the Trivoli cyclothem, and neither of these cyclothems has much sandstone in the vicinity of Carlinville. A test boring on the Robley farm in the NW ¼ sec. 3, T. 10 N., R. 6 W. (Shaw Point Twp.) has been utilized for water supply, and the water is said to come from a depth of 365 feet, apparently from the Carbondale group.

The great majority of the farm wells in the quadrangle obtain water from the glacial drift at depths of from 14 to 40 feet. Across the north part of the quadrangle, west from Girard, the average depth of 15 wells is 42 feet. From Girard to Palmyra the average depth to water in 13 wells, including 3 wells of more than ordinary depth, is 31 feet. The average depth of 10 wells west of Nilwood, including some exceptionally deep for farm wells, is 35 feet. Across the quadrangle in the latitude of Schoper the average depth is 19 feet for 16 wells. East and west from Carlinville the average depth of 26 wells is 21 feet.

Springs. — Springs are abundant in the quadrangle. They issue from pockets of sand and gravel in the till and from buried soil zones or pre-Illinoian surfaces. The rain water, slowly descending through the compact till, moves laterally from high toward low areas. At low spots in the till where permeable material is exposed, groundwater may move to the surface and form a spring.

Sources of Municipal Supplies. — Virden and Girard were at one time dependent on shallow geologic sources but at present both cities get their water from Springfield reservoir. Palmyra, Nilwood, and other villages do not have municipal systems; private wells draw water from shallow zones. Carlinville obtains its water supply from a reservoir on Honey Creek.

APPENDIX A — GEOLOGIC SECTIONS

Thickness
Ft. In.

Geologic section 1.[a]*—Southernmost exposure in west bank of tributary of Massa Creek, in the SE ¼ SW ¼ sec. 10, T. 11 N., R. 8 W. (South Palmyra Twp.) (fig. 7)*

Pennsylvanian system, McLeansboro group
Trivoli cyclothem
4 Sandstone, calcareous, micaceous, platy, light yellow gray, spotted with brownish weathering stains, fine-grained; beds of variable thickness 1
3 Sandstone, light yellow gray, mottled with brown patches where fresh, brown where weathered; evenly bedded in thin strata; bears some ripple marks 2   8
Scottville cyclothem
2 Shale, sandy, olive green where fresh, weathering to a grayish green, alternating with lenses of yellow micaceous sand; proportion of shale increases downward 3   9
1 Shale, slightly micaceous, light gray, relatively free from sand, decidedly soft, jointing not conspicuous; contains a few flattened concretions of clay "ironstone" . 3   5

Geologic section 2.—Outcrop in south bank of Bear Creek, in the SE ¼ NE ¼ SW ¼ sec. 21, T. 10 N., R. 8 W. (Bird Twp.)

Pennsylvanian system, McLeansboro group
Trivoli cyclothem
2 Shale, noncalcareous, locally nongritty, drab to brown where fresh, weathering to mottled brown and gray; prominently jointed, with other vertical fractures parallel to the joint-planes. 12–15
1 Sandstone, calcareous, earthy, locally very argillaceous, dark gray when fresh, dense, fossiliferous 1   6

Geologic section 3.[a]*—West bank of tributary to Massa Creek in the NE ¼ SW ¼ sec. 10, T. 11 N., R. 8 W. (South Palmyra Twp.)*

Pennsylvanian system, McLeansboro group
Trivoli cyclothem
8 Shale, silty, noncalcareous, light yellow gray, evenly laminated, thin- to medium-bedded 7   6
7 Shale, noncalcareous, nongritty, light gray, evenly bedded, with a few light blue-gray slightly calcareous "ironstone" concretions containing fragments of *Calamites* and other plants 6

[a]Geologic sections 1 and 3 are a quarter mile apart, and the base of No. 3 is about 5 feet vertically above the top of No. 1; how much if any stratigraphic interval between them is not known.

6 Shale, noncalcareous or faintly calcareous, black, hard, fossiliferous 1½–2
5 Shale, thin-bedded; contains bony coal . . . .   ¼
4 Coal (No. 8), hard, bright, somewhat bony 5–6
3 Underclay, dark gray, soft . . . 2
2 Underclay, medium to light gray, noncalcareous in upper 6 inches . 1
1 Underclay, medium gray, harder than the above, slickensided, contains small calcareous concretions   9

Geologic section 4.—Excavation for abutment at east end of bridge of State Highway No. 108 across Bear Creek, NE ¼ SE ¼ SE ¼ sec. 20, T. 10 N., R. 8 W. (Bird Twp.)

Pleistocene system
Illinoian stage
4 Drift, ... about 35
Pennsylvanian system, McLeansboro group
Trivoli cyclothem
3 Shale, slightly gritty, slightly calcareous, micaceous, slightly carbonaceous, medium gray weathering to light brown or yellow, massive but showing lamination planes 12
2 Coal (No. 8), bright, discontinuous . . . .   ¼
1 Shale, more massive than that above, dark gray, weathering lighter 8

Geologic section 5.—Outcrop in the northeast wall of a gully, in the SW ¼ SW ¼ SE ¼ sec. 21, T. 10 N., R. 8 W. (Bird Twp.)

Pleistocene system
Illinoian stage
6 Glacial drift . . . . (not measured)
Pennsylvanian system, McLeansboro group
Carlinville cyclothem
5 Shale, calcareous, slightly micaceous, gray mottled with brown, poorly bedded; contains irregular "chunky" calcareous nodules 1   6
4 Sandstone, very calcareous, argillaceous, micaceous, medium gray mottled with brown, somewhat friable, in three fairly distinct ledges. 2
Trivoli cyclothem
3 Shale, light gray, laminated . .   4
2 Shale, medium dark gray mottled with brown, massive, but more platy and with increasing mica content near the base   6
1 Shale, blue gray, compact, brittle, well-bedded . . . . 6–8+

	Thickness	
	Ft.	In.

Geologic section 6.—Outcrop along west valley wall of stream, in the SE ¼ SW ¼ sec. 23, T. 12 N., R. 8 W. (North Palmyra Twp.)

Pleistocene system
11   Loess, glacial drift, etc. . . . . .(not measured)
Pennsylvanian system, McLeansboro group
  Carlinville cyclothem
10   Shale, calcareous, light olive gray,
       soft, flaky   8
9   Limestone, brownish y e l l o w,
       weathering to a rusty limonite
       brown, dense, fossiliferous . . .   3–4
8   Shale, very calcareous, yellow
       gray, soft, thin-bedded and poor-
       ly bedded, fossiliferous 3–5½
7   Limestone, medium gray, weath-
       ering to light yellow brown, hard,
       massive, fossiliferous, slightly
       shaly at top   1
6   Shale, medium gray, weathering
       to buff, lower portion darker gray
       but not black, thin and platy at
       base, nonlaminated at top . . .   8
5   Limestone, medium gray, hard,
       impure, shaly at top and base,
       few carbonaceous traces 1   10
4   Shale, calcareous, or shaly lime-
       stone, hard, probably fossiliferous   8
3   Shale, medium to dark gray, thin-
       bedded, becoming harder and
       slightly more massive at base . 1   7
2   Shale, sandy, bluish gray, some-
       what more massive than the
       overlying. 3   6
1   Sandstone, slightly calcareous,
       gray, medium-grained; interbed-
       ded with shales, noncalcareous,
       sandy, yellow gray, laminated . 3

Geologic section 7.—Outcrop in east-west gully in the NE ¼ NE ¼ sec. 27, and the NW ¼ NW ¼ sec. 26, T. 12 N., R. 8 W. (North Palmyra Twp.)[a]

Pennsylvanian system, McLeansboro group
  Carlinville cyclothem
14   Shale, noncalcareous, olive gray,
       medium soft, thin-bedded; con-
       tains small clay "ironstone" con-
       cretions, especially in the upper
       two-thirds; sparingly fossiliferous,
       jointing not conspicuous 13
       Covered interval 2
13   Limestone, medium gray where
       fresh, yellow brown on weathered
       surfaces, abundantly mottled
       with ramifying trails or impres-
       sions, poorly bedded 2   6
12   Shale, calcareous, light gray,
       grading down to medium gray .   6
11   Limestone, gray, massive, well
       jointed, parallel jointing   4
       Covered interval   6
10   Limestone, gray, massive, fossil-
       iferous   11
9   Shale, soft, fossiliferous   5

	Thickness	
	Ft.	In.

8   Limestone, argillaceous, medium
       gray, with some poorly preserved
       fossils   3
7   Shale, calcareous, gray, soft . .   1
6   Coal, upper half good quality,
       lower half bony   1
5   Shale, calcareous, dark gray, soft,
       thin - bedded; bedding surfaces
       covered with impressions of stems
       and excellently preserved leaves . 1   6
4   Shale, slightly gritty, blue gray;
       impressions of stems with no
       leaves 1   6
3   Sandstone, yellow gray, somewhat
       cross-bedded, some alternation of
       thicker and thinner beds 3   6
2   Sandstone, medium gray, some-
       what mottled with limonitic
       blotches, cross-bedded (sugges-
       tive of a channel sandstone) . .   5
1   Shale, noncalcareous, sandy, mi-
       caceous, thin-bedded, with con-
       sistent, easterly dip in the cross-
       bedding   5

Geologic section 8.—Outcrop along stream, SE ¼ NE ¼ sec. 34, T. 12 N., R. 8 W. (North Palmyra Twp.) (fig. 11)

Pennsylvanian system, McLeansboro group
  Carlinville cyclothem
12   Limestone, light to medium gray,
       weathering light yellow brown,
       massive, well jointed, fossilifer-
       ous; upper 6 to 7 inches shaly . . 2   6
11   Shale, calcareous, green gray to
       dark gray, soft; some limestone
       nodules in upper portion   4
10   Shale, slightly calcareous, black,
       hard, well laminated, fossilifer-
       ous, with irregular or winding
       traces of light gray shale, possibly
       worm tubes   4
9   Limestone, somewhat earthy,
       medium to dark gray, massive,
       fossiliferous, bedding indistinct .   8
8   Shale, strongly calcareous, dark
       gray, soft, poorly laminated, with
       calcareous nodules   4
7   Shale, black, thin-bedded, some
       layers with coaly luster, inter-
       bedded with light gray clay or
       shale; locally contains pyritic
       l i m e s t o n e concretions, with
       Chonetes and crinoid stems,
       around which the laminae bend,
       bony coal up to ¼ inch thick and
       traces of fossil plants, mainly
       stems 1–2½
6   Shale, slightly calcareous, dark
       gray, soft, thin-bedded, flaky;
       bedding surfaces covered with
       poorly preserved plant impres-
       sions; bony coal layers up to 1/32
       inch thick; pyritic concretions
       containing fossil traces and cri-
       noid stems 4½

Thickness
Ft.   In.

5 Shale and bony coal, thin-bedded, with clay partings ¼ inch thick . 1

4 Shale, slightly gritty, noncalcareous, medium gray to green gray, soft 6

3 Shale, light olive gray, poorly bedded. 6

2 Sandstone, calcareous, medium gray, indistinctly bedded at top but well bedded below, the massive beds especially calcareous. . 1   6

1 Sandstone, shaly, less calcareous than above, fine-grained, thin-bedded, some strata ripple-marked 1   3

Geologic section 9.—Outcrop in the SW ¼ NW ¼ sec. 10, T. 11 N., R. 8 W. (South Palmyra Twp.)

Pennsylvanian system, McLeansboro group
  Carlinville cyclothem

12 Limestone, medium gray, hard, massive, crystalline, sparsely fossiliferous, joint-planes distinctly developed 3   7

11 Shale, nearly clay at top, very calcareous, yellow gray to buff, grading down into light gray, soft, crumbly, poorly laminated, occasional streaks of carbonaceous material 6

10 Shale, calcareous, black, with brown gray spots on bedding-surfaces, well laminated, but not extremely hard, gypsum crystals on lamination surfaces, fossiliferous 3

9 Shale, black, similar to the above, but softer, bedding surfaces covered with small, irregular whitish masses, some of which appear to be sulfates, others possibly shell fragments 1

8 Limestone, shaly, dark gray, slightly fossiliferous, with small gray limestone nodules 1½

7 Limestone, medium blue gray, somewhat massive, fossiliferous; marked by black, carbonaceous stainings, somewhat suggestive of "fucoids," possibly molluscan trails 9½

6 Shale, strongly calcareous, light yellowish gray, poorly laminated. 3

5 Shale, black, finely laminated, with plant remains on bedding surfaces 1

4 Shale, slightly silty, noncalcareous, medium to fairly dark gray, with leaf and stem impressions, and thin stringers of coal, possibly carbonized logs, up to 1½ inches thick 1   9

3 Shale, sandy, light gray, beds somewhat thicker and more irregular than the overlying, rusty stains on bedding surfaces . . . 1   7

Thickness
Ft.   In.

2 Shale, slightly sandy, mostly non-calcareous, medium gray, softer than the overlying, thin-bedded; black, carbonaceous, sometimes woody lenses 1   10

1 Sandstone, gray to light blue gray, wavy bedding, fairly hard, calcareous beds inter-stratified with noncalcareous beds; micaceous and carbonaceous flakes on bedding surfaces 1

Geologic section 10.—Outcrop along the east bank of Hurricane Creek, in the SE ¼ SE ¼ sec. 30, T. 10 N., R. 7 W. (Carlinville Twp.)

Pleistocene system
10 Loess and till . . . . (not measured)
Pennsylvanian system, McLeansboro group
  Carlinville cyclothem

9 Limestone, dark gray, weathering to light yellow gray with red splotches. 4   7

8 Shale, calcareous, black, fairly hard, thin-bedded, slightly fossiliferous 1–6

7 Limestone, dark gray, dense, with occasional calcite crystals, becoming laminated and argillaceous, with rusty brown patches in the lower two inches 5

6 Shale, slightly calcareous, green gray, with some thin carbonaceous flakes almost coal 3

5 Coal, bony to sub-lustrous . . . 1

4 Shale, slightly calcareous, slightly gritty, dark gray, thin-bedded, with abundant leaf and stem impressions. 3

3 Shale, micaceous, light to medium gray, soft, thin-bedded, with excellently preserved plant impressions and small calcareous concentrations along bedding planes 9

2 Sandstone, micaceous, calcareous in the more massive beds, medium gray, fine-grained, friable; strata range from less than an inch up to six inches in thickness; flakes of carbonaceous material 3   6

1 Sandstone, micaceous, medium blue gray with streaks of yellow gray, flaky . . . . 6+

Geologic section 11.—Outcrop along Macoupin Creek, in the NW ¼ NW ¼ SE ¼ sec. 4, T. 9 N., R. 7 W. (Brushy Mound Twp.)

Pleistocene system
  Illinoian stage
3 Till, dark gray, crumbly, about . 5–8
Pennsylvanian system, McLeansboro group
  Carlinville cyclothem
2 Limestone, dark blue gray weathering dull brown, slightly mottled, dense, slightly fossiliferous . 6–8

Thickness
Ft.   In.

1 Shale, micaceous, dark gray weathering brown, sparsely fossiliferous, carbonaceous traces . 11–12

Geologic section 12.—Outcrop along Macoupin Creek, in the NE ¼ sec. 34, T. 10 N., R. 7 W. (Carlinville Twp.)

Pennsylvanian system, McLeansboro group
  Carlinville cyclothem
6 Shale, yellow   2
5 Shale, black   1
4 Limestone, dark gray, darker than the overlying shale 6½
3 Shale, very calcareous, brown gray, poorly bedded; poorly developed concretionary band at its base 3   2
2 Clay or shale, silty, noncalcareous, light olive gray, blocky fracture, fairly soft   10
1 Shale or siltstone, sandy, olive gray or brown, fairly well bedded   10

Geologic section 13.—Outcrop in west bank of Massa Creek, in the SW ¼ sec. 2, T. 11 N., R. 8 W. (South Palmyra Twp.)

Pennsylvanian system, McLeansboro group
  Carlinville cyclothem
5 Limestone, coarsely crystalline, purple red weathering to brown on bedding planes; thin-bedded, flaggy, locally cross-bedded; very fossiliferous, bearing *Myalina* sp., a few brachiopods, gastropods, and fragments of carbonaceous material; grades to   4
4 Shale, calcareous, carbonaceous, apparently made up almost entirely of the same kind of carbonaceous material that occurs in the overlying limestone, dark gray or black, evenly bedded . .   4
3 Limestone, gray where fresh, oxidized to brown on bedding planes, fossiliferous, in strata about ¼ inch thick . . . . .   3±
2 Shale, calcareous, medium gray, platy, breaking in large fragments, slightly wavy laminae, some mica flakes   8
1 Shale, calcareous, medium gray, poorly bedded, more massive than shale above . . . . 6 (exposed)

Geologic section 14.—Clay pit, Carlinville Tile Company in south part of Carlinville, in the NE ¼ SE ¼ SW ¼ sec. 33, T. 10 N., R. 7 W. (Carlinville Twp.)

Pleistocene system
  Illinoian or pre-Illinoian (Kansan ?) stage
7 Till, leached, deep yellow brown, starchy fracture; abundant chert pebbles 3

Thickness
Ft.   In.

6 Sand, calcareous, coarse, yellow brown, lenticular 0–2   6
5 Till, calcareous, buff to yellow gray 0–1   2
  Pre-Illinoian (Kansan ?) stage
4 Till, noncalcareous except slightly calcareous in the basal part, gray, tough, sticky, and putty-like when wet; contains a few boulders and scattered pebbles of basic igneous rock and siliceous pebbles   7
Pennsylvanian system, McLeansboro group
  Carlinville cyclothem
3 Shale, noncalcareous, light bluish gray, free from grit, simulates massive bedding but is laminated; contains large clay-ironstone concretions, slightly calcareous . . .   10
2 Shale, noncalcareous, dark gray, firm, massive   4
1 Limestone (underlying the floor of the pit), dark gray, massive .   6

Geologic section 15.—Outcrop along west bank of Macoupin Creek, W ½ NE ¼ NW ¼ sec. 35, T. 10 N., R. 7 W. (Carlinville Twp.)

Pleistocene system
9 Alluvium (possibly outwash or drift) . . . . (not measured)
Pennsylvanian system, McLeansboro group
  Burroughs beds
8 Shale, slightly gritty, noncalcareous, micaceous, light green gray; platy, fossiliferous horizon about 10 inches above base 1   10
7 Limestone, purple brown, coarsely crystalline, crinoidal, cross-bedded; interlaminated with greenish shales; somewhat arenaceous, occasionally marked by carbonaceous traces; carries large Productid brachiopods; slumps down in large irregular blocks . . 1   10
6 Sandstone, grayish, lenticular, mud-cracked and ripple-marked, interlaminated with thin lenses of greenish very fine-grained noncalcareous shales; at its base locally what seems to be a decomposed limestone with many fossils, chiefly gastropods   10
  Carlinville cyclothem
5 Shale, slightly calcareous, olive gray, evenly bedded 7
4 Shale, blue gray, better bedded than above; contains concretions, medium purple gray, pyrite concretions, and a few black, carbonaceous impressions, possibly plant remains (?); marked near the base by peculiar, crescent-shaped points or fractures . . . 8   8
3 Limestone, very nodular, fossiliferous 1½
2 Shale, medium gray . . . . . .   ½
1 Limestone 1   6

Thickness Ft. In.

Geologic section 16.—*Combination of three outcrops, two on the west valley wall of Massa Creek north of the bridge and the third in the east valley wall south of the bridge, in the SW ¼ sec. 25, T. 12 N., R. 8 W. (North Palmyra Twp.)*

Pleistocene system
  Illinoian stage
  6 Till, noncalcareous, yellow, starchy fracture . . . (not measured)
Pennsylvanian system, McLeansboro group
  Burroughs beds (possibly either Macoupin cyclothem or McWain sandstone)
  5 Shale, noncalcareous, green to brown . . . 6
  4 Sandstone, very calcareous, micaceous, light vivid green . . . 1
  3 Sandstone, micaceous, noncalcareous, brown with gray and black mottlings or inclusions 3-4
  Carlinville cyclothem
  2 Shale, slightly silty, noncalcareous, green gray weathering to brown and green; a few ironstone concretions at its base; close-set, nearly vertical jointings 13
  1 Shale, noncalcareous, brown . . 20

Geologic section 17.—*Outcrop in Burroughs branch NE ¼ NW ¼ SW ¼ sec. 27, T. 10 N., R. 7 W. (Carlinville Twp.)*

Pleistocene system
  Illinoian stage
  9 Soil, till, etc., well weathered . . 3
Pennsylvanian system, McLeansboro group
  Macoupin cyclothem
  8 Shale, slightly calcareous, light yellow gray to yellow brown, with limonite-coated calcareous concretions 1
  7 Sandstone or sandy shale, very calcareous, light yellow gray; poorly bedded and more shaly near the top; few fossils . . . 2
  6 Sandstone, dark gray when fresh weathering to yellow gray and tan; more massive than overlying bed; interbedded with hard calcareous beds containing some fossils possibly derived from older beds; suggestive locally of an impure sandy limestone 5   9
  Burroughs beds
  5 Shale, sandy, green gray where fresh, gray when weathered, few fossils 1
  4 Limestone, green to brown gray where fresh, weathering brown, crystalline, fossiliferous 3-6
  3 Sandstone, calcareous, micaceous, green gray, medium-bedded, fossiliferous 1
  2 Limestone, somewhat sandy, medium to brown gray, weathering rusty, crystalline, crinoidal, fossiliferous; includes masses of soft shaly material 2-4

Thickness Ft. In.

Carlinville cyclothem
  1 Shale, sandy, slightly calcareous, green gray, soft, platy, nonfossiliferous . . . . 1+

Geologic section 18.—*Outcrop in the south bank of Macoupin Creek, southwest of old bridge on abandoned highway, in the NE ¼ SW ¼ NW ¼ sec. 2, T. 9 N., R. 7 W. (Brushy Mound Twp.)*

Pennsylvanian system, McLeansboro group
  Burroughs beds
  5 Shale, calcareous, micaceous, platy, gray . . . . . (not measured)
  4 Limestone, crystalline, dark gray, weathers to a red brown, nodular, fossils poorly preserved . . . . ½-¾
  3 Sandstone, calcareous, micaceous, gray mottled with brown, poorly bedded, slabby, ripple-marked . 1
  2 Sandstone, very calcareous, micaceous, fine-grained, gray, weathers to brown, ripple-marked   3
  Carlinville cyclothem
  1 Shale, slightly calcareous, micaceous, gray to brown, poorly bedded; weathers into irregular polygonal subtabular blocks . . 6+

Geologic section 19.—*Outcrops along small tributary of Macoupin Creek, in SW ¼ SE ¼ sec. 35, T. 10 N., R. 7 W. (Carlinville Twp.) and NE ¼ NW ¼ sec. 2, T. 9 N., R. 7 W. (Brushy Mound Twp.)*

Pennsylvanian system, McLeansboro group
  Shoal Creek cyclothem
  53 Limestone, dense, light gray, poorly bedded, nodular, abundantly fossiliferous 7
  52 Limestone, more massive in upper part than in lower part, green gray; grades into overlying limestone 1   6
  51 Shale, clayey, calcareous, soft, gray, fossiliferous 1   1
  50 Shale, bituminous, locally calcareous, subcuboidal jointing; contains worm borings 1   6
  49 Shale, somewhat calcareous, black, hard; contains conodonts, fish scales and spines, and occasional flakes of gypsum . . . 2   3
  48 Shale, calcareous, black, hard, poorly bedded, fossiliferous . . .   5-6
  47 Shale, calcareous, brown gray, fossiliferous . . . .   ½
  46 Shale, clayey, calcareous, dark gray, sparsely fossiliferous; limestone concretions, up to 4 inches in thickness and 12 inches across and containing pyritized fossils, occur near the top 2   2
  45 Shale, clayey, noncalcareous, light gray, "iron" stained 2½
  44 Clay, noncalcareous, poorly bedded, light to medium blue gray, some suggestion of lamination .   8½

No.	Description	Ft.	In.
43	Clay, harder than the above, slightly calcareous, medium gray		7
42	Limestone, shaly, medium gray, fossiliferous		¼
41	Shale, slightly calcareous, gray .		2
40	Limestone, very fossiliferous . .		½
39	Shale, slightly calcareous, medium gray; contains marine fossils and traces of wood		9
38	Limestone, blue gray, highly fossiliferous; contains *Murchisonia* or *Worthenia* (?)	1½–2	
37	Shale, blue gray, thin-bedded, fossiliferous; contains *Leda* and carbonaceous woody material . .		4
36	Limestone, medium to dark blue gray; contains *Aviculopecten, Murchisonia, Bellerophon*		½–1
35	Shale, light blue gray, thin-bedded		5
34	Limestone, medium to dark blue gray, sub-crystalline, moderately fossiliferous, with *Aviculopectens* and gastropods		1½
33	Shale, blue gray, thin-bedded . .		1–1½
32	Limestone, dark blue gray, fossiliferous		1½
31	Shale, blue gray		1½
30	Limestone		¼–½
29	Shale, medium gray		5½
28	Shale, highly calcareous, dark gray to black, soft, fossiliferous; contains *Aviculopecten, Leda,* etc.	1	10
27	Limestone; contains numerous thin-shelled pelecypods		½
26	Coal, bright; irregular discontinuous band		¼
25	Clay, noncalcareous, brown gray; joints filled with secondary calcite		7
24	Clay, calcareous, dark gray . . .		3
23	Clay, light gray streaked with brown grading down to medium gray; contains small rounded or uneven limestone nodules . . .	1	10
22	Clay, calcareous, light green gray; contains nodules up to 2 inches in diameter; grades into the overlying shale	1	6
21	Shale, calcareous, green gray, poorly laminated above, becoming well and thinly bedded below, with limestone concretions up to 6 or 8 inches in maximum diameter	1	10
20	Shale, calcareous, sandy, almost a sandstone or siltstone, green gray		3–4

Macoupin cyclothem

No.	Description	Ft.	In.
19	Limestone, dense, reddish, nodular, poorly bedded, fossiliferous .		8
18	Shale, calcareous, light blue gray, well bedded; contains flattened oval green-gray limestone concretions up to 1½ inches thick near top	1	

No.	Description	Ft.	In.
17	Shale, calcareous, micaceous, with lens-like masses of calcareous sandstone, green gray, slightly fossiliferous and containing peculiar trail markings	1	
16	Limestone, blue gray when fresh, weathers to streaky rusty brown, densely crystalline, fossiliferous, nodular		5
15	Shale, calcareous, micaceous, green gray, with scattered discoidal clay-ironstone concretions displacing the shale laminae by their growth; joints filled with calcite and limonite		4
14	Limestone, crinoidal, granular, greenish, brownish, and dark gray; abundantly fossiliferous, with *Spirifer cameratus*		8
13	Shale, calcareous, fossiliferous, green gray, lower part dark gray, with flattened oval nodules of crystalline limestone		6–8
12	Shale, slightly calcareous, dark gray, fairly hard, unevenly bedded; contains some brownish limestone concretions in lower part	1	
11	Shale, black, hard, laminated; contains conodonts	1	1½
10	Clay, calcareous, dark gray, soft, fossiliferous; contains *Productids*		1½
9	Coal, bright bands, dull on bony laminated planes, thin-bedded .		8
8	Underclay, noncalcareous . . .		½
7	Underclay, green gray; small calcareous concretions near base		9
6	Underclay, calcareous, blue to green gray, starchy fracture; varies from nongritty to sandy; contains calcareous nodules up to ¼ inch in diameter and very small crystals of marcasite . . .		6
5	Shale, calcareous, slightly silty, blue or green gray, thin-bedded, platy; contains calcareous concretions	1	6
4	Sandstone and sandy shales, interbedded, micaceous, highly calcareous (the top 2 inches is especially calcareous), blue gray, ripple-marked; thin- to medium-bedded; the thicker beds have peculiar markings	2–3	

Burroughs beds

No.	Description	Ft.	In.
3	Shale, somewhat micaceous, light green gray, thin-bedded; locally includes thin beds of siltstone, sandstone, and limestone . . .	2	5
2	Limestone, sandy, blue gray, crystalline, irregularly bedded, very fossiliferous, with occasional pebbles of limestone material .	3	
1	Sandstone, noncalcareous, fine-grained, interlaminated with greenish shale		1–9

	Thickness	
	Ft.	*In.*

Geologic section 20.—Outcrop in gully, just north of the culvert in Highway No. 4, NE corner NW ¼ NW ¼ sec. 2 T. 9 N., R. 7 W. (Brushy Mound Twp.)

Pennsylvanian system, McLeansboro group
  Macoupin cyclothem

7	Sandstone and sandy shales, inter-bedded, very calcareous, micaceous, blue gray, ripple-marked	2–3	
	Burroughs beds		
6	Limestone, blue gray, fossiliferous	3–4	
5	Siltstone, soft.		1
4	Sandstone, grayish, hard, ripple-marked	¼–½	
3	Siltstone, grayish, soft		1
2	Sandstone, grayish, hard, ripple-marked	¼–½	
1	Siltstone, medium gray, medium hard.	1½	

Geologic section 21.—Outcrop on gully slope, in the SW ¼ NW ¼ NW ¼ sec. 35, T. 10 N., R. 7 W. (Carlinville Twp.)

Pennsylvanian system, McLeansboro group
  Macoupin cyclothem

6	Shale, weathered, dark brown .	5	
5	Coal "blossom," much weathered	?	
4	Clay, noncalcareous	10	
3	Clay, calcareous, green gray . .	2	
2	Shale, calcareous, containing irregular dense fossiliferous nodules up to 4–5 inches	4	
	Burroughs beds (?)		
1	Limestone, densely crystalline, gray, weathers to brown; includes quartz pebble	1+	

Geologic section 22.—Outcrops in two gullies, in the SE ¼ NE ¼ sec. 26, T. 10 N., R. 7 W. (Carlinville Twp.)

Pleistocene system

17	Drift and loess	40±	
	Pennsylvanian system, McLeansboro group		
	Shoal Creek cyclothem		
16	Limestone, gray weathering to yellow and pink, densely crystalline, fossiliferous, poorly bedded; upper massive bed 14 to 16 inches thick, with uneven, striated surface; beds below nodular and slabby with green gray calcareous shaly partings up to 3 to 4 inches thick	6–8	
15	Shale, green gray, thinly bedded, nonfossiliferous; contains three bands of concretions	1	6
14	Shale, dark gray, thinly and evenly bedded, blocky; no fossils in the upper part	1	10
13	Shale, black, hard, laminated; contains gypsum crystals, plant remains (?), and conodonts . .	2	7
12	Shale, dark gray to black, fairly hard, platy		8

11	Limestone (concretionary band), dark blue gray, dense, hard . .		2–5
10	Shale, dark gray, medium-bedded		5–8
9	Shale, noncalcareous, light green gray to medium gray, thinly and poorly bedded, soft	1	9
8	Limestone, blue gray, small fossils		1–3
7	Shale, similar to No. 9 but contains abundant calcareous nodules up to ½ inch in thickness .		3
6	Clay, slightly calcareous, with calcareous nodules.		2¼
5	Clay, slightly calcareous, slate-colored or medium gray, with small rounded nodules up to ½ inch	1	6
	Covered interval	3±	
4	Shale, calcareous, olive gray . .	2–3	
	Macoupin cyclothem		
3	Limestone, gray weathering to brown, crystalline, fossiliferous .		4
	Covered interval	14±	
2	Shale, calcareous, gray to olive drab, thin, platy, soft	1	6+
	Covered interval	4±	
	Burroughs beds		
1	Limestone, gray, crystalline, crinoidal		1

Geologic section 23.—Outcrop in west bank of Macoupin Creek, in the NW ¼ NE ¼ sec. 25, T. 10 N., R. 7 W. (Carlinville Twp.)

Pleistocene system

15	Alluvium, with well oxidized sand and some pebbles suggestive of "bronze" chert	6+	
	Pennsylvanian system, McLeansboro group		
	Macoupin cyclothem		
14	Shale, non-gritty, slightly calcareous, with a few micaceous beds, green gray with mottling of brown, thin-bedded, blocky .	3	2
13	Limestone, blue gray weathering to tan, medium to coarsely crystalline, moderately fossiliferous, crinoidal; in two massive beds with a 2-inch slabby, irregular bed between them and with wide-spaced joints, forming large slabs when slumped (Macoupin limestone)	1	2
12	Shale or clay, calcareous, dark gray, fossiliferous, splintery fracture		4
11	Coal, locally in beds ¼- to ½-inch thick		3–5
10	Clay, noncalcareous, dark gray stained brown; irregular contact at base		½–2
9	Coaly seam, discontinuous . . .		¼
8	Clay, silty, noncalcareous, blue gray mottled with brown, soft .		3
7	Clay or shale, non-gritty, calcareous, dark green gray; bears plant remains; grades to	2	
6	Coal.		¼

Thickness
Ft.   In.

5   Limestone, earthy, fine-grained, dark to purplish gray, weathers brownish yellow; smooth upper surface; contains small high-spired gastropods and abundant plant remains   10–30
4   Shale, clayey, very calcareous, coaly, dark greenish gray, discontinuous   1   4
3   Clay, calcareous, dark brownish gray, discontinuous   6
    Burroughs beds
2   Limestone, nodular, dense, tough, bluish gray, weathers gray and yellow   2
1   Limestone, bluish gray, more massive than the above . . . .   3+

Geologic section 24.—Outcrop in southeast bank of Macoupin Creek, in the NW ¼ NE ¼ NE ¼ sec. 25, T. 10 N., R. 7 W. (Carlinville Twp.)

Pleistocene system
12   Alluvium . . . . (not measured)
Pennsylvanian system, McLeansboro group
    Macoupin cyclothem
11   Limestone, slabby, nodular, crinoidal, bluish gray, mottled with black stains (Macoupin limestone)   6–8
10   Clay, yellow gray, nodular, crumbly, fossiliferous, thoroughly oxidized   1–3
9   Coal   4–9
8   Clay, noncalcareous, yellow gray to brown, fairly hard 2½–5½
7   Coal, discontinuous . . . .   ¼
6   Clay or shale, dark gray to brown, carbonaceous   6–10
5   Limestone, shaly, dark gray, abundant small fossils   2
4   Clay, calcareous, olive gray to brownish gray, fossiliferous . . .   6
3   Shale, black, coaly ½–1
2   Clay, calcareous, brown gray, hard, blocky, fossiliferous . . .   8
    Burroughs beds
1   Limestone, dark gray to black weathering to gray mottled with yellow brown, nodular, fossiliferous   3–4

Geologic section 25.—Outcrop in the W ½ sec. 2, T. 9 N., R. 7 W. (Brushy Mound Twp.)

Pleistocene system
20   Loess and drift . . . .   20±
Pennsylvanian system, McLeansboro group
    Shoal Creek cyclothem
19   Clay, slightly calcareous, dark gray, massive; contains a few scattered calcareous nodules . .   2   4
    Macoupin cyclothem
18   Clay or shale, light gray tinged with green, weathering yellow and brown; contains gray calcareous nodules up to 1″ in diameter, slightly fossiliferous   1   4

Thickness
Ft.   In.

17   Limestone, dense, nodular, gray to brownish gray, reddish brown when weathered, slightly fossiliferous   1   3
16   Shale, slightly sandy, calcareous, finely micaceous, light gray, thinbedded; contains a few gray limestone concretions   1   8
15   Limestone concretionary band, brownish gray weathering to reddish brown, dense, hard   3–4
14   Shale, slightly sandy, calcareous, finely micaceous, light bluish gray, thin-bedded   9
13   Limestone, brownish red, finely crystalline, thin-bedded, slabby, fossiliferous . . . .   ½
12   Shale, calcareous, finely micaceous, gray-tinged blue, thinly and evenly bedded   1   5
11   Limestone concretionary band, brownish . . . .   ½
10   Shale, calcareous, finely micaceous, gray-tinged blue, thinly and evenly bedded . . . . . .   1+
    Covered interval, spring comes out at this horizon in gully floor .   1±
9   Limestone, brownish red, coarsely crystalline, crinoidal, well and evenly bedded, flaggy, very fossiliferous (Macoupin limestone) . . .   10
    Covered interval   1   6
8   Shale, noncalcareous, olive gray mottled dark, thin-bedded . . .   1
7   Shale, noncalcareous, dark gray to black, fairly hard, thin-bedded, probably platy   1   3
6   Shale, noncalcareous, greenish yellow, no fossils observed . . .   3
5   Coal, bony 5½
4   Clay, coaly, dark gray, soft . . .   ½
3   Clay, noncalcareous, light gray, yellow on fractured surfaces, soft, crumbly 6½
2   Clay, noncalcareous, gray, rusty on fracture surfaces, more blocky than above   6
1   Clay, calcareous, yellowish gray; contains small gray calcareous nodules . . . .   3+

Geologic section 26.—Outcrop 50 yards downstream from outcrop measured in geologic section 27, in the NE ¼ sec. 35, T. 10 N., R. 7 W. (Carlinville Twp.)

Pennsylvanian system, McLeansboro group
    Macoupin cyclothem
11   Limestone (Macoupin limestone)   1   6
10   Shale, greenish gray   1
9   Shale, dark gray to black, slip-fracture surfaces   8
8   Shale, dark, hard, evenly laminated   10
7   Shale, noncalcareous, dark gray, nonfossiliferous, massive, slip-fracture surfaces; abundant dark gray clay "ironstone" concretions   11
6   Shale, black, soft, flaky 1½
5   Coal 5½

	Thickness Ft.	In.

4 Clay, carbonaceous, dark gray, soft . . . . — 2½

3 Clay, dark gray stained with limonite; slip-fracture surfaces . — 10

2 Clay, light gray, stained with limonite, soft . . . . — 8½

1 Clay, calcareous, bluish gray . . — 3

Geologic section 27.—Outcrop in the southeast bank of Macoupin Creek, NW ¼ SE ¼ NE ¼ sec. 35, T. 10 N., R. 7 W. (Carlinville Twp.)

Pleistocene system

13 Drift, loess, and alluvium . . (not measured)

Pennsylvanian system, McLeansboro group
 Macoupin cyclothem

12 Limestone, brownish gray to pinkish gray, crystalline, crinoidal, fossiliferous (Macoupin limestone) 8

11 Shale, greenish gray, soft, flaky . 7

10 Shale, grayish black to black, firm, massive, with slip fractures 9

9 Shale, silty, black with thin laminae of gray, hard, evenly laminated 11

8 Shale, dark gray to black, massive, slip fractures 7

7 Limestone, bluish gray, crystalline, abundantly fossiliferous, well jointed. 1 1

6 Clay, highly calcareous, soft, crumbly, concretionary 9

5 Shale, dark gray, soft, platy, with carbonaceous traces and pyritized wood 1–1¼

4 Coal, poor quality, highly weathered 6½–8

3 Clay, noncalcareous, dark gray to black, soft, crumbly 1

2 Clay, noncalcareous, gray, stained with limonite on fracture planes 11½

1 Clay, calcareous, gray, firm, massive . . . . 3+

Geologic section 28.—Outcrop in east bank of Macoupin Creek about 100 yards north of State Highway No. 108, north of the turn in the NE ¼ SE ¼ sec. 26, T. 10 N., R. 7 W. (Carlinville Twp.)

Pleistocene system

13 Alluvium, containing water-worn pebbles of quartzite, chert, quartz and jasper, suggestive of the "Lafayette" gravel . . . . . . (not measured)

Pennsylvanian system, McLeansboro group
 Macoupin cyclothem

12 Shale, somewhat silty, mostly noncalcareous, grayish green to yellow gray, thin, platy, with small fossils . . . . 1+

11 Limestone, bluish gray, medium crystalline, crinoidal, very fossiliferous; massive 4-inch bed in upper part, thinner slabby beds in lower part; contains occasional pockets of calcareous clay (Macoupin limestone) 2 6

10 Clay, shaly, greenish gray . . . — 3

	Thickness Ft.	In.

9 Limestone, similar to that above, but poorly bedded (Macoupin limestone) . . . . — ½–4

8 Shale, non-gritty, calcareous, greenish gray, thinly and poorly bedded; limy band near the top — 10

7 Shale, carbonaceous, dark gray; contains fossiliferous calcareous nodules . . . . — 10

6 Shale, noncalcareous, very carbonaceous, brown to black, poorly bedded; locally contains bony coal near the base and concretions near the top . . . . — 8

5 Shale, noncalcareous, black, hard, laminated, sheety, fossiliferous (conodonts) . . . . — 10–11

4 Shale, noncalcareous, dark gray to black, hard, less sheety than the above; contains a few *Pectens* — 5–6

3 Coal, poor quality . . . . . . — 4–7

2 Clay, dark purplish gray, abundantly stained with limonite . . — 3

1 Clay, slightly gritty, carbonaceous, noncalcareous, dark gray . 1 —

Geologic section 29.—Outcrop near mouth of short tributary to Macoupin Creek, in the NW ¼ SE ¼ sec. 25, T. 10 N.,R. 7 W. (Carlinville Twp.) (see geologic section 33)

Pennsylvanian system, McLeansboro group
 McWain sandstone

20 Sandstone, massive, light greenish gray, stained with limonite, friable, slightly cross-bedded; contains a few thin lenses of carbonaceous material and occasional calcareous micaceous "ironstone" concretions; irregular contact at base 4–5

19 Shale, micaceous, gray, soft, discontinuous laterally 8–12

18 Sandstone, same as (20) above, interbedded with shales; crossbedded 1–3

17 Sandstone, micaceous, coarsegrained, with abundant carbonaceous seams 3–6

 Macoupin cyclothem

16 Shale, bluish gray to olive gray, thin-bedded, blocky 2

15 Shale, gray, rusty, with discontinuous bank of fossiliferous gray concretions . . . . — 10

14 Shale, calcareous, bluish gray to olive gray, fossiliferous, with gastropods predominant 3 8

13 Shale, bluish gray, thin-bedded, blocky, few fossils 6 6

12 Clay ("clod"), rusty gray and greenish, soft, fossiliferous, fossils small . . . . — 1–3

11 Limestone, gray, medium to coarsely crystalline, crinoidal, more massive in upper 4 to 6 inches, slabby below, well jointed, fossiliferous (Macoupin limestone) . . . . — 6–9

		Thickness	
		Ft.	*In.*

10 Clay, calcareous, bluish gray, discontinuous laterally   0–1
9 Coal, hard, lustrous   4–5
8 Clay, calcareous, greenish gray to olive gray, grades to . . .   ¼–½
7 Coal, bony, in lenses, and . . . .   ½–¾
6 Clay, slightly calcareous, dark gray ½–1
5 Clay or shale, slightly calcareous, light bluish gray to purplish gray, indistinctly bedded; occasional dark flakes   1
4 Limestone, dark gray to black, hard, thin-bedded or laminated; contains plant impressions or remains and invertebrate fossils .   4
3 Clay, very calcareous, yellow gray with yellowish patches, soft   3–4
2 Coal, slabby, bony, in occasional lenses ⅛–1
1 Clay, slightly silty, very calcareous, dark to light greenish gray, hard, with root traces . . . . .   8+

Geologic section 30.—Outcrop along west bank of Macoupin Creek, in the SE ¼ NW ¼ SE ¼ sec. 24, T. 10 N., R. 7 W. (Carlinville Twp.)

Pennsylvanian system, McLeansboro group
  Macoupin cyclothem
7 Shale, gray, soft, thinly bedded .   2
6 Limestone, gray, fossiliferous, platy; some carbonaceous matter present locally (Macoupin limestone)   1   5
5 Limestone and calcareous shale, interbedded, thin beds   8
4 Coal, with about 1-inch dark shale parting   9
3 Underclay and shale, calcareous, bluish, soft, thin-bedded   1   8
2 Limestone, gray to dark gray, with thin bands of black shale, platy   3
1 Shale, calcareous, dark gray, soft, thin-bedded   1   6

Geologic section 31.—Outcrop along east bank of Macoupin Creek, in the SE ¼ SE ¼ NE ¼ sec. 24, T. 10 N., R. 7 W. (Carlinville Twp.)

Pennsylvanian system, McLeansboro group
  Macoupin cyclothem
6 Limestone, fossiliferous, nodular (Macoupin limestone)   10
5 Shale   1   3
4 Coal   6
3 Shale   3
2 Limestone, hard, slabby   5
1 Shale, calcareous   1

Geologic section 32.—Outcrop in upper part of gully, in the SE ¼ SE ¼ NE ¼ sec. 35, T. 10 N., R. 7 W. (Carlinville Twp.)

Pleistocene system
15 Loess and drift   40–55

		Thickness	
		Ft.	*In.*

Pennsylvanian system, McLeansboro group
  Shoal Creek cyclothem
14 Limestone, gray weathering to pink, slabby, nodular, poorly bedded   6
    Covered interval . . . .   3±
13 Shale, black, hard, fossiliferous, platy   9
12 Shale, dark greenish gray, softer than the above, poorly bedded .   1   1
11 Limestone (concretionary band), dark bluish gray, dense   4
10 Shale, dark gray, platy, fairly well bedded, no fossils observed .   1   3
9 Shale, very calcareous, gray, fossiliferous, crumbly   3
8 Limestone, gray, soft; small fossils . . . .   ¼–½
7 Shale, gray to light gray 1½
6 Limestone, gray, crystalline, soft, fossiliferous . . . .   ¼–½
5 Shale, dark gray weathering to light bluish gray, thinly and evenly bedded; few fossils   1   6
4 Shale, similar to the above, greenish to dark gray . . . .   1+
3 Shale, very calcareous, light olive gray; contains small calcareous concretions   8
    Covered interval   3–4
  Macoupin cyclothem
2 Limestone, light bluish gray, weathering to brownish, somewhat nodular, silty   4–6
1 Shale, olive gray, silty, with some calcareous concretions   1   3

Geologic section 33.—Outcrop at head of southwest branch of gully, in the SW ¼ NW ¼ SE ½ sec. 25, T. 10 N., R. 7 W. (Carlinville Twp.) (see geologic section 29)

Pennsylvanian system, McLeansboro group
  McWain sandstone
3 Sandstone, soft, friable, fine-grained, olive gray to brownish gray, with large flakes of mica and carbonaceous matter on bedding planes, in beds 6-8 inches thick .   8–10
  Macoupin cyclothem
2 Shale, fairly micaceous, light greenish gray, thinly and evenly bedded   2   8
1 Shale, calcareous, some layers more silty and micaceous than others, gray to dark gray with greenish tinges; abundantly fossiliferous with small gastropods, spired and plano-spiral, pelecypods, brachiopods, and a few horn corals in zone about one foot from top; also small pyrite concretions of irregular shape and gray ironstone concretions up to 1x2x2 inches . . . .   3+

Thickness
Ft.   In.

Geologic section 34.—Outcrop downstream from geologic section 33 in east bank of main gully below junction of two branches, in the SE ¼ sec. 25, T. 10 N., R. 7 W. (Carlinville Twp.)

Pennsylvanian system, McLeansboro group
McWain sandstone
5 Sandstone, micaceous, greenish gray, soft, friable, mealy; abundant carbonaceous material on some bedding planes; beds usually 1–2 inches thick, lowest bed firm, 4–5 inches thick 6
Macoupin cyclothem
4 Shale, sandy, micaceous, greenish gray 4
3 Shale, some beds sandy, micaceous, greenish gray, thinly bedded 1   2
2 Shale, calcareous, light to dark olive gray, with some micaceous sandy beds that are more irregular than others, the whole fairly evenly bedded, breaking out in blocks; very fossiliferous, with gastropods, pelecypods, brachiopods, and many small fossils, especially at base . . . . 6+
1 Shale, noncalcareous, bluish gray to greenish gray, evenly bedded, thin to medium beds 2   10

Geologic section 35.—Outcrop in tributary to Macoupin Creek, in the center of the NW ¼ sec. 36, T. 10 N., R. 7 W. (Carlinville Twp.) (fig. 22)

Pleistocene system
18 Loess, till, etc . . . . (not measured)
Pennsylvanian system, McLeansboro group
Shoal Creek cyclothem
17 Limestone, gray, weathering to light gray and pink, sublithographic, fossiliferous, poorly bedded 1   6
16 Limestone, gray, hard, very fossiliferous, flaggy 4   6
15 Clay, calcareous, greenish gray, soft 5
14 Limestone, light bluish gray, hard, brittle, fossiliferous, slabby, with very thin shaly partings . . 2   2
13 Clay, calcareous, yellow, soft . . 5
12 Limestone, gray to bluish gray, dense, hard, fossiliferous 6
11 Limestone, argillaceous, gray, slightly decomposed 3
10 Shale or clay, calcareous, yellow gray, soft 3
9 Shale or clay, calcareous, medium gray with dark patches, fossiliferous, massive; contains calcareous concretions 1
   Covered interval 1
8 Shale, calcareous, dark gray, mottled, somewhat flaky . . . 1   2
7 Shale, noncalcareous, black, hard, platy 5

Thickness
Ft.   In.

6 Shale, dark greenish gray, poorly to thinly bedded 6
5 Shale, black, hard, fossiliferous, in large plates : 5
4 Shale, dark gray to black, thinly bedded, softer than above; locally contains coaly inclusions . . 7
3 Shale or clay, calcareous, mottled light and dark greenish gray, poorly bedded 1   5
2 Limestone (concretionary band), dark bluish gray, hard, nonfossiliferous 2–3
1 Shale, calcareous, mottled greenish gray and olive gray . . . . 6+

Geologic section 36.—Outcrops in the floor of valley, in the NW ¼ NE ¼ sec. 16, T. 11 N., R. 7 W. (South Otter Twp.) (fig. 15)

Pennsylvanian system, McLeansboro group
Shoal Creek cyclothem
9 Limestone, bluish gray, weathering to reddish brown or buff, tough, brittle, fossiliferous, nodular, peculiar wavy bedding; upper surface honeycombed with solution pits, some up to 1 or 2 inches across; well-developed joints, the more prominent striking N. 57° E., the less so N. 36° W. 3   6
8 Limestone, light gray, fine-grained, brecciated or nodular . . 1
7 Limestone, light greenish gray to brownish gray, fairly coarsely crystalline, crinoidal; weathered surfaces covered with bryozoans, crinoids, and other fossils . . . 4
6 Clay, calcareous, greenish gray to brownish gray, fossiliferous . . 1±
5 Limestone, greenish gray to brownish gray, crinoidal, upper portion soft, lower portion hard . 10±
4 Shale, noncalcareous, black, hard, laminated; contains conodonts . 4
3 Clay, noncalcareous, dark gray . ¼
2 Clay, noncalcareous, yellowish . 1
1 Clay, slightly gritty, slightly calcareous above, highly so below, bluish gray, stained with limonite; small round nodules of CaCO₃, probably secondary . . 9–11

Geologic section 37.—Outcrop along the west bank of stream, in the SE ¼ sec. 9, T. 11 N., R. 7 W. (South Otter Twp.)

Pleistocene system
3 Loess and till . . . . (not measured)
Pennsylvanian system, McLeansboro group
Shoal Creek cyclothem
2 Limestone, somewhat earthy, dark gray tinged with pink, densely crystalline, hard 1¼–2¼
1 Limestone, earthy, dark gray, sparingly fossiliferous, poorly bedded 3   6+

	Thickness	
	Ft.	In.

Geologic section 38.—Outcrop in gully north of and parallel to the abandoned railroad in the SE ¼ NW ¼ NW ¼ sec. 36, T. 10 N., R. 7 W. (Carlinville Twp.)

Pleistocene system
  Wisconsin stage
6 Loess, probably Peorian . . . . 3±
  Illinoian stage
5 Gumbotil, characteristic . . . . 3±
4 Till (horizon 5 of the weathering profile), prominently jointed . . 3–4
  Kansan (?) stage
3 Till, thoroughly leached and oxidized, mottled reddish brown and brown, gummy . . . . 2±
2 Till, slightly silty, leached and oxidized, buff to reddish brown, compact; contains a few pebbles of chert and quartz (horizon 3 of the weathering profile) 2 6
1 Till, calcareous, oxidized, buff to brown, compact, moderately pebbly 6–7

Geologic section 39.—East bank of Sugar Creek, in the SE ¼ NE ¼ sec. 30, T. 10 N., R. 6 W. (Shaw Point Twp.)

Pleistocene system
  Illinoian stage
7 Till, sandy in the basal part, buff to bluish gray, leached to a depth of 10½ feet; contains large fragments of wood 20
  Yarmouth stage
6 Sand, gravelly, slightly calcareous, yellowish, cross-bedded . . 3 4
5 Sand or silt, very fine-grained, calcareous, yellow gray, mottled with diffusion bands of limonite, wavy laminae; variable thickness 1 8
4 Humus zone, containing fibers of wood and twigs, undulatory band ½
3 Silt, calcareous, dark gray, fossiliferous (see Appendix C); contains fragments of wood and is interbedded with sand lenses . . 3–7
  Kansan (?) stage
2 Till, calcareous, dark gray to nearly black, with fragments of greenish sandy shale incorporated in the basal part; sandy and silty near the top, with fragments of coal 7
Pennsylvanian system, McLeansboro group
  Shoal Creek (?) cyclothem
1 Shale, slightly calcareous, with a small amount of mica, platy, dark gray to drab, the upper part sandy and green . . . . 2+

Geologic section 40.—On west bank of Cottonwood Creek, near the center of sec. 28, T. 10 N., R. 6 W. (Shaw Point Twp.)

Pleistocene system
  Recent stage

	Thickness	
	Ft.	In.

11 Soil, surficial material, dark brown to black, apparently developed directly upon the till, no loess present, grading downward into No. 10. 10
  Illinoian stage
10 Gumbotil, brown with gray splotches, gray more abundant in the upper part, stained locally with deep brown, porous; contains a few chert pebbles and one pebble of fine-grained basic igneous rock 3 4
9 Till, leached, brown; pebbles small; somewhat regular limonitic band at the base (horizon 3 of weathering profile) 6
8 Till (horizon 4 of weathering profile) 10–12
  Yarmouth stage
7 Sand, fine-grained, silty, calcareous, yellow gray mottled with gray bands; irregular wavy laminae 2
6 Sand, coarser than the above, calcareous, locally leached, yellow gray, more oxidized and more regularly laminated than above, with prominent red bands . . . 2 4
5 Sand, fine-grained, calcareous, yellow gray, regularly laminated, with conspicuous reddish brown iron oxide at the base 1 4
4 Sand or silt, fine grained, calcareous, yellow gray, wavy laminations, with regularly spaced, oblique brown or nearly black stains 6
3 Silt, calcareous, gray, marked as the material above, and probably representing the unoxidized portion of it; 4 or 5 inches above its base is a prominent, nearly horizontal black band that may be a humus stain, although no woody material is observed; the whole unit is undulatory, either deposited on an irregular surface or distorted by pressure, possibly of ice movement 8
2 Humus zone, poorly developed, the woody fibers mixed with silt and till, nonfossiliferous, calcareous except locally, irregular . . . 6
  Kansan (?) stage
1 Till, calcareous, dark gray, mixed with silt and sand at the top; zone of iron oxide about 6 inches from the top . . . . 6±

Geologic section 41.—Outcrop in east wall of gully, in the NE ¼ SE ¼ sec. 16, T. 11 N., R. 7 W. (South Otter Twp.) (fig. 16)

Pleistocene system
  Illinoian stage

| | | *Thickness* | | | | *Thickness* | |
| | | Ft. | In. | | | Ft. | In. |

4 Till, calcareous, dark brown, fracture planes coated with limonite, with small siliceous pebbles in gravel pockets, and with woody fragments near the base . . . . 10±

Yarmouth (?) stage

3 Silt, or fine sand, calcareous, gray with limonite mottling and black streaks; oxidized in the upper portion; of variable thickness and laterally intergrades with a "fat" clay containing wood fragments, the clay as much as two inches thick 3–6

2 Humus horizon, somewhat peaty, calcareous, sandy, containing occasional twigs and branches, fossiliferous, with fragile pelecypod and gastropod shells (Appendix C) 2–3

Kansan (?) stage

1 Till, or "till-like" material, calcareous, drab or dark gray, marked with abundant slope cleavage planes, which are stained with limonite; pebbles scattered, soft, crumbly, possibly concretions; locally this horizon passes laterally into a silt which is highly fossiliferous and is sometimes more than a foot thick . . . . . . 3+

Geologic section 42.—Exposure on north side of small gully in the NW ¼ NW ¼ NE ¼ sec. 16, T. 11 N., R. 7 W. (South Otter Twp.)

Pleistocene system

Illinoian stage

4 Till, calcareous except at top, brown . . . . 3+

Yarmouth stage

3 Silt, calcareous, ash gray, limonitic stains, highly fossiliferous, pelecypods, water-laid (?) 2–2½

2 Silt, calcareous, brown to brownish red, nonfossiliferous, water-laid (?), with irregular contact beneath on sand, gravel, and till? 1

Kansan (?) stage

1 Till, calcareous, deep brown, pebbly . . . . 1+

Geologic section 43.—Exposure on the north side of the principal gully, in the NE ¼ SE ¼ sec. 9, T. 11 N., R. 7 W. (South Otter Twp.)

Pleistocene system

Illinoian stage

7 Till, calcareous, gray to drab, weathering to gray and brown, with carbonized wood; oxidized at its contact with the underlying material . . . . 10±

Yarmouth stage

6 Silt, calcareous, yellow brown . 2–3

5 Humus horizon, considerably mixed with clay, slightly calcareous, fairly persistent 1–2

4 Silt, calcareous, carbonaceous, dark gray to drab; fossiliferous . 1   2

3 Sand, calcareous, yellowish brown, medium- to coarse-grained, with some medium coarse gravel; slightly laminated, gummy . . . 1   2

Kansan (?) stage

2 Till, calcareous, chocolate brown, sticky and plastic at the top . .   4–6

1 Till, calcareous, somewhat sandy, pebbly, drab, very hard, containing many deep red, thoroughly oxidized, iron-bearing pebbles . 3–4(exposed)

Geologic section 44.—Exposure in stream valley, in the SE ¼ SW ¼ sec. 14, T. 11 N., R. 8 W. (South Palmyra Twp.)

Pleistocene system

Illinoian stage

7 Till, dark gray to black, humusstained, somewhat plastic, containing a few siliceous pebbles . 2–3½

6 Till, leached in the upper part, calcareous in the lower part, yellow with brown mottling; contains siliceous pebbles . . . 1   3

5 Gravel, or pebble band, locally silty, variable in thickness . . .   2–8

4 Clay, leached, yellow brown, containing well disintegrated igneous rocks, and some humus fillings . 1   6

3 Till, calcareous, yellow gray, with many pebbles up to 2 inches in diameter . . . .   6±

2 Silt, calcareous, gray, with lenses of coarser yellow or reddish brown sand, with a slight amount of gravel 2

Kansan (?) stage

1 Till, hard, calcareous, blue gray, pebbles sparse; striated surface . 2–3+

Geologic section 45.—Outcrop in gully, in the SW ¼ NE ¼ SW ¼ sec. 3, T. 11 N., R. 8 W. (South Palmyra Twp.)

Pleistocene system

Illinoian stage

4 Till, calcareous, brown, slightly jointed, relatively free from pebbles 6–7

Kansan (?) stage

3 Till, leached, yellow brown; chert and other siliceous pebbles . . .   3–8

2 Till, calcareous   5

1 Till, calcareous, brown, with a few scattered cobbles, and containing local patches of bright green, silty material . . . . . . 2+

Note: About a quarter of a mile upstream from this measured section there is a layer of peat between the Illinoian and Kansan tills. The thickness of the leached zone on the Kansan till also increases upstream.

Thickness
Ft.   In.

Geologic section 46.—Exposure in wall of gully, together with record of auger boring, in the SE ¼ sec. 10, T. 11 N., R. 7 W. (South Otter Twp.) (figs. 4 and 17)

Pleistocene system
  Recent stage
  8 Soil . . . . (not measured)
  Wisconsin stage
  7 Loess   4–5
  Illinoian stage
  6 Till (weathering profile well shown) 17
  Yarmouth stage
  5 Clay, light gray, fossiliferous . .   ½
  4 Peat, compact, locally fibrous, soft molluscan shells on surface .   2   4
*3 Silt, peaty, calcareous, dark gray and brownish, dank odor   2
*2 Silt, peaty, noncalcareous, dark gray and brownish, sandy in the basal foot   2   9
*1 Gravel, silty, calcareous, dark gray, contains fragments of bluish shale and igneous pebbles (stopped on cobble, water rose in hole).   6–8

Geologic section 47.—Pleistocene deposits, cut bank near the fork of tributaries, center of the NE ¼ sec. 27, T. 10 N., R. 7 W. (Carlinville Twp.), upstream from the Womac division (abandoned) of the Chicago and Alton R. R. (figs. 18 and 19)

Pleistocene system
  Illinoian stage
  7 Till, thoroughly leached and oxidized, but not typical gumbotil, brown, grades downward into . .   0–6
  Yarmouth stage
  6 Sand, fine-grained, leached, yellow brown, bedding indistinct; penetrated by some carbonized roots   6
  5 Gravel and coarse sand, oxidized and leached; base undulatory and irregular, thoroughly cemented in lower 6 inches   10–12
  4 Sand, fine-grained, calcareous, but leached slightly near the top, brown, laminated, disturbed by shearing and slumping   2   3
  3 Sand, fine-grained, calcareous, gray. . . . .   ¼–½
  2 Humus, fibrous, occasional small twigs or roots 0–½
  Kansan (?) stage
  1 Till or till-like material, silty, brownish to yellowish brown, with pebbles of quartz, chert, flint, and at least one limestone pebble, roughly 2x2x1½ inches; very fossiliferous at the top, carrying also "pipestem" concretions; tends to cleave into platy fragments . .   1   8

———
*Record of auger boring.

Thickness
Ft.   In.

Geologic section 48.—Exposure in west bank of tributary to Otter Creek, in the NE ¼ SW ¼ sec. 22, T. 11 N., R. 8 W. (South Palmyra Twp.) about one mile upstream from Antioch Church.

Pleistocene system
  Recent stage
  5 Soil, loessial, slightly leached . .   2   6
  Illinoian stage
  4 Till, compact, blue gray, weathering to buff, pebbly but relatively free from cobbles, slightly oxidized, especially calcareous near the middle   9   6
  3 Sand, coarse-grained, brownish yellow, well oxidized   2
  2 Clay, noncalcareous, yellow-gray, well oxidized, slightly stained with some black mineral . . . .   4±
  1 Till, similar to that above the sand, calcareous, blue gray, large cobbles, occasional boulders . . 18

Geologic section 49.—Exposure in south wall of cut on State Highway 108, in the NW ¼ sec. 36, T. 10 N., R. 7 W. (Carlinville Twp.)

Pleistocene system
  Recent stage
  6 Soil and slope-wash, leached . .   3–4
  Illinoian stage
  5 Till, oxidized, yellowish   1
  4 Till, yellowish gray, containing an included mass of interbedded silt and till, attaining dimensions of 4x10 feet, the included mass highly oxidized 12
  3 Silt, calcareous, gray, forming a nest around the base of the inclusion above, maximum thickness   1   3
  2 Till, calcareous, dark bluish gray, interbedded with light gray silt, the interbedded units variable in thickness. . . . .   1±
  1 Till, calcareous, gray, but tinted with streaks of bluish gray and purplish gray, and includes lenses of oxidized silty sand   8–10

Geologic section 50.—Exposure along southeast bank of Sugar Creek, in the NW ¼ NW ¼ sec. 13, T. 12 N., R. 7 W. (North Otter Twp.) Items 1-3 are record of auger boring in bottom of stream valley adjacent to the bank.

Pleistocene system
  Wisconsin stage
  14 Loess or soil, dark, loosely coherent, more or less porous   1   1
  13 Loess or clay, leached, dark brownish gray to yellowish brown, tenacious, starchy fracture   3   2
  12 Loess or clay, leached, brownish yellow gray, looser in texture than the above, less porous, ferruginous streaks and concretions . .   1

		Thickness	
		Ft.	In.

11 Loess or silt, leached, yellowish gray to gray, tenaceous   2

10 Loess or silt, leached, grayish mottled with brown; contains some humus material near the base; occasional pebbles in basal part   2   9

9 Clay, yellow, sticky, in discontinuous irregular patches . . . .   3±

8 Silt, noncalcareous, slightly sandy in places, gray   2

7 Silt, noncalcareous, sometimes sandy, yellow, occasional small, siliceous pebbles; either overlies or is interbedded with ½–1

Sangamon stage

6 Humus, slightly silty, noncalcareous, apparently free from roots or twigs, discontinuous . . . . .   ½

5 Silt, noncalcareous, dark gray to black, containing occasional fragments of humus material   1   8

4 Marl, with small molluscan shells in great abundance (Appendix C)   6

3 Silt, gray with occasional patches of green, very fossiliferous, especially in the upper part, some horizons more fossiliferous than others 5½–6

2 Peat, locally calcareous   6

1 Silt, moderately calcareous; contains occasional fragments of humus . . . .   ?

Geologic section 51.—Exposure along north side of road about a tenth of a mile east of the Washington School, in the SE ¼ sec. 18, T. 12 N., R. 7 W (North Otter Twp.)

Pleistocene system
　Recent stage
7 Soil . . . . (not measured)
　Wisconsin stage
　　Peorian substage
6 Loess, slightly gritty, leached, light gray with much brown ferruginous staining, gumbo-like in the upper four feet   6
　　Farmdale substage
5 Soil (?) or loess, weathered, noncalcareous ½–2
4 Loess, noncalcareous, gray with a faint bluish or greenish tint and with chocolate mottling   6–10
　Illinoian stage
3 Soil zone, chocolate brown, nonresistant, starchy, pebbly   2–4
2 Gumbotil, gray, mealy, with pellets and pebbles. . . . .   1+
1 Gumbotil, gray, plastic, hackly .   1–2+

Geologic section 52.—Exposure along highway, in the SW ¼ sec. 26, T. 10 N., R. 7 W. (Carlinville Twp.)

Pleistocene system
　Wisconsin stage
　　Peorian substage

		Thickness	
		Ft.	In.

7 Soil, black, grading downward to   6–8

6 Silt or silty clay, light brown . .   6

5 Silt-clay, brown slightly mottled with gray   2–3

　Farmdale substage

4 Clay-silt or silt-clay, mottled gray and brown   1

3 Silt, laminated, gray with a little brown mottling; pebbles up to ¼ inch common   1   6–8

2 Silt, clayey, brown, purplish or chocolate tint, pebbles up to ½ inch abundant; grades to. . . .   2

1 Clay, silty, brown with a very little gray mottling, pebbles abundant   1   6

Geologic section 53.—Record of auger boring in ditch along northeast side of State Highway No. 4, on terrace in the SE ¼ sec. 34, T. 10 N., R. 7 W. (Carlinville Twp.)

Pleistocene system
　Wisconsin stage
　　Peorian substage
10 Loess, in roadside cut . . . . .   6±
9 Loess   1   8
8 Loess, with brownish buff particles coated with white silty material   1   8
7 Silt, pebbleless, slightly plastic, light buff, with iron nodules. . .   2   6
　　Farmdale substage
6 Silt, less plastic, no pebbles, slightly friable, buff, mottled . .   10
5 Silt, more compact, dark brownish buff   2
4 Silt, sandy, occasional pebbles, dark to brownish buff   2
　Illinoian (or Sangamon) stage
3 Sand, fine-grained, much weathered, sticky, mottled buff and drab, gumbo-like in lower part .   1   6
2 Sand and gravel, much weathered, brownish buff to drab brown in lower part, gumbo-like. . . .   6
1 Sand and gravel, calcareous; auger stopped on bedrock (Carlinville limestone)   6

Geologic section 54.—Generalized section in the former Moody Co. clay pit, in the NE ¼ sec. 32, T. 10 N., R. 7 W. (Carlinville Twp.) (fig. 21)

Pleistocene system
　Recent stage
8 Soil, granular, crumbly, light gray.   8
　Wisconsin stage
7 Loess, noncalcareous, yellowgray to light brown with some orange colored patches, slightly plastic   1
6 Loess, noncalcareous, gray mottled with light yellow brown, tenaceous, plastic, scattered manganese (?) pellets of pea size . . .   1   4

	Thickness	
	Ft.	In.

5 Loess, yellow gray mottled with deep orange patches, tough tenaceous, similar to the above, but cracks in "joint-clay" fractures on drying . . . . 1 | 1
4 Loess, light yellow gray mottled with vivid orange, slightly gumbo-like, some slight fracturing . 11–13
3 Loess, dark brownish gray, tough, tenaceous; resembles till but is pebble-free . . . . 1 | 1
2 Loess (explored by auger), silty near the base, noncalcareous, dark to medium gray . . . . . 5 | 6
Illinoian stage
1 Till, dark gray, leached for 9 feet 10 | 6

	Thickness	
	Ft.	In.

Geologic section 55.—Exposure in gully, in the NE ¼ sec. 26, T. 11 N., R. 8 W. (South Palmyra Twp.)

Pleistocene system
  Recent stage
2 Soil, noncalcareous, ash gray, flour-like texture, occasional grains of muscovite and chert, with a few limonitic (?) pellets . 1 | 8
Wisconsin stage
1 Loess, noncalcareous, buff mottled to yellow gray, plastic, gumbo-like; exposed 2

APPENDIX B — RECORDS OF DEEP WELLS

The following records of 11 wells, mine shafts, or test borings in the Carlinville quadrangle provide typical information about the subsurface geologic formations in the quadrangle. Similar records of many other wells in and around the quadrangle, as well as for the rest of the state, are available for reference and loan at the State Geological Survey, Urbana, Illinois.

1. Fuller and Turner—Chamness No. 1 well, SW ¼ SW ¼ NE ¼ sec. 4, T. 9 N., R. 6 W. (Honey Point Twp.) [a]

Elevation 638 feet

	Thickness Ft.	Depth Ft.
Pleistocene system		
No samples.	20	20
Sand, medium- to fine-grained, subrounded.	64	84
Pennsylvanian system		
Sandstone, sideritic, light green to light brown, fine- to very fine-grained, shaly at base	15	99
Shale, micaceous, green, soft to firm	5	104
Limestone, partly argillaceous, gray to light gray mottled, extra fine- to some coarse-grained. . .	10	114
Sandstone, micaceous, light gray, fine- to very fine-grained, some argillaceous and carbonaceous partings	9	123
Shale, silty, sandy, micaceous, partly carbonaceous, gray . . .	25	148
Limestone, light brown, very fine-grained; coal	2	150
Sandstone, calcareous, light gray, very fine-grained, grades to shale partings, silty, sandy, and carbonaceous	45	195
Shale, silty, micaceous, gray, soft	20	215
Limestone, light buff to brown, very fine-grained	4	219
Sandstone, calcareous, micaceous, very fine- to fine-grained	21	240
Shale, gray to dark brown to black, weak; coal	10	250
Sandstone, micaceous, gray, fine-grained	10	260
Limestone, light gray to buff, very fine- to medium-grained, dense	5	265
Shale, smooth, green, firm	5	270
Limestone, buff, extra fine-grained	7	277
Shale, partly silty and carbonaceous, gray, weak	38	315
Coal, black, shiny	5	320
Shale, gray brown, firm	5	325

[a]Sample study by Paul Herbert, Jr.

	Thickness Ft.	Depth Ft.
Limestone, white to buff to light gray, extra fine-grained	15	340
Sandstone, calcareous, micaceous, greenish gray, fine- to very fine-grained; siderite nodules and cement	28	368
Sandstone, micaceous, fine- to coarse-grained, incoherent, water-bearing	44	412
Shale, silty, micaceous, dark brown; coal, black, shiny . . .	8	420
Sandstone, silty, very micaceous and carbonaceous, gray, fine- to very fine-grained, some very argillaceous partings.	15	435
Shale, silty, micaceous, carbonaceous, gray, firm	25	460
Shale, very dark gray to black, hard.	7	467
Coal, black, shiny	4	471
Limestone, gray to brownish gray, fine- to coarse-grained, partly fossiliferous.	4	475
Coal, black, shiny.	5	480
Shale, light gray buff to buff, smooth	13	493
Sandstone, micaceous, greenish gray, very fine-grained, hard, many spherules, black; grades to shale at base, silty, sandy, micaceous, light gray	17	510
Coal, black, shiny to dull. . . .	4	514
Sandstone, very fine- to fine-grained, incoherent	10	524
Shale, finely micaceous, black, hard.	20	544
Shale, very silty and micaceous, light brown, weak	10	554
Shale, silty, finely sandy, micaceous, carbonaceous, gray . . .	10	564
Sandstone, light gray, very fine-grained, hard; shale partings . .	10	574
Shale, silty to sandy, micaceous, carbonaceous, gray; sandstone lenses	21	595
Shale, sandy, micaceous, carbonaceous, very light gray; siderite, brown, dense	13	608
Sandstone, slightly calcareous, fine- to medium- and coarse-grained, some very silty; water-bearing	42	650
Shale, silty, micaceous, carbonaceous, light gray	4	654
Conglomerate, chert, weathered, white, yellow, purple; much pyrite; sandy; some sandstone. . .	8	662
Sandstone, very fine- to coarse-grained, some sandstone aggregate; some siderite, sandy	3	665
Mississippian system		
Iowa series		
Meramec group		
Ste. Genevieve formation		

	Thick-ness Ft.	Depth Ft.
Limestone, sandy, oolitic, pyritic, very light gray, very fine-grained	5	670
Limestone, very sandy, oolitic, very light gray, very fine-grained	10	680
St. Louis formation		
Limestone, sandy to silty, white to very light buff, very fine-grained, dense	53	733
Dolomite, gray to brownish gray, very fine-grained, crystalline	15	748
Limestone, cherty, light gray to light brownish gray, very fine-grained, with dolomite, very light gray, crystalline, very fine-grained in lower 20 feet	47	795
Limestone, light brownish gray, lithographic, dense	15	810
Limestone, sandy, light buff gray, extra fine-grained	5	815
Dolomite, cherty, gray buff, very fine- to fine-grained, dense	5	820
Limestone, cherty, light gray, very fine- to medium-grained, rough texture	20	840
Limestone, light gray to light brown, lithographic to extra fine-grained, dense	30	870
Dolomite, light gray to light brown to brown, fine-grained, partly crystalline	18	888
Limestone, very light gray, lithographic, with chert, white to very light gray, speckled buff in lower 9 feet	21	909
Salem formation		
Dolomite, light brown, very fine- to extra fine- grained, crystalline	21	930
Dolomite, silty, argillaceous, gray	15	945
Limestone, gray to light gray buff mottled, coarse-grained, fossiliferous, with *Endothyra*	20	965
Dolomite, very light gray, very fine-grained, crystalline; argillaceous partings; coarse-grained calcareous fossils	25	990
Dolomite, calcareous, light gray to gray mottled, very fine-grained, partly crystalline, very fossiliferous, with chert, milky, and quartz in lower 15 feet	30	1,020
Osage group		
Warsaw formation		
Shale, very silty, calcareous, gray; grades to limestone, sandy, argillaceous, gray to pale green	17	1,037
Sandstone, calcareous, slightly glauconitic and pyritic, light gray, fine-grained	18	1,055
Shale, sandy, silty, light gray, weak	15	1,070

	Thick-ness Ft.	Depth Ft.
Sandstone, calcareous, slightly glauconitic and pyritic, partly very silty, light gray, fine- to very fine-grained	25	1,095
Shale, silty, light gray, soft	5	1,100
Shale, silty, light gray; very many calcareous fossil fragments	55	1,155
Keokuk-Burlington formations		
Limestone, cherty, partly argillaceous, light gray to gray mottled, coarse-grained, fossiliferous; interbedded shale	20	1,175
Siltstone, calcareous to siliceous, very cherty, very light gray to gray; chert, clear to white, many sponge spicules	21	1,196
Limestone, cherty, partly oolitic, white to buff, medium- to coarse-grained, fossiliferous	29	1,225
Limestone, cherty, silty, gray to light gray, fine-grained	15	1,240
Limestone, cherty, white, medium- to coarse-grained	38	1,278
Fern Glen formation		
Siltstone, calcareous, slightly argillaceous and glauconitic, cherty, white to very pale green	17	1,295
Limestone, siliceous to cherty, silty, slightly glauconitic, white, medium- to coarse-grained	25	1,320
Limestone, very cherty, partly silty, white to very pale pink and green, medium- to fine-grained	25	1,345
Limestone, very cherty, white to some pale green, medium- to coarse-grained	25	1,370
Limestone, very argillaceous, cherty, very pale green to white, with some shale, silty, calcareous, pale green	30	1,400
Limestone, very silty, pink to buff mottled, medium-grained, grades to some shale, pink	5	1,405
Kinderhook group		
Chouteau formation		
Limestone, white to very light gray, very fine- to some medium-grained	23	1,428
Hannibal formation		
Maple Mill member		
Shale, silty, greenish gray to gray	15	1,443
Hamburg member		
Shale, silty, brown	7	1,450
Shale, very silty, gray to light brown with brown organic flakes; some siltstone, gray	15	1,465
Limestone, very oolitic, very light gray, fine-grained; oolites coarse, gray-centered	4	1,469
Siltstone, calcareous, gray	11	1,480
Shale, very silty, gray, grades to some siltstone	35	1,515

	Thickness Ft.	Depth Ft.

Grassy Creek formation
Shale, silty, dark brown; contains spores .... 35 — 1,550
Shale, silty, very light gray to dark brown; contains organic flakes and spores; a little pyritic sandstone at base .... 14 — 1,564

Devonian system

Wapsipinicon formation
Sandstone, calcareous, white, medium-grained........ 8 — 1,572
Limestone, sandy, very light gray, extra fine-grained, slightly fossiliferous .... 15 — 1,587
Limestone, light brown, extra fine-grained; some dark brown partings .... 8 — 1,595
Dolomite, sandy, light gray to gray to brown, very fine-grained, crystalline, partly vesicular 20 — 1,615
Dolomite, cherty, sandy, very light buff, very fine-grained .. 5 — 1,620
Limestone, white to very light buff, lithographic to earthy; abundant free siderite grains . 10 — 1,630

Silurian system

Niagaran series
Dolomite, very cherty, light buff, very fine-grained .... 60 — 1,690
Dolomite, light gray with slight greenish tint, very fine-grained; very cherty, slightly shaly in upper 15 feet and with trace of shale, green, fine-grained, dolomitic, in lower 15 feet .... 50 — 1,740
Dolomite and limestone, light gray with greenish tint, dense to very fine-grained .... 35 — 1,775
Limestone, dolomitic, white to light gray to buff, faintly green, lithographic to very fine-grained, dense .... 60 — 1,835
Limestone, slightly dolomitic, white to light gray, pink and orange flecks, fine-grained .. 45 — 1,880
Dolomite, white to light gray, very fine-grained ...... 15 — 1,895

Alexandrian series

Sexton Creek formation
Dolomite, cherty, light gray, dense, very fine-grained, large glauconitic fragments; becomes very cherty downward.... 20 — 1,915
Edgewood formation (?)
Dolomite, very cherty, slightly silty, light brown, fine-grained 30 — 1,945

Ordovician system

Cincinnatian series

Maquoketa formation
Shale, light grayish green to darker green, some brownish in lower 10 feet, weak ...... 86 — 2,030
Shale, carbonaceous, pyritic, brown, firm .... 15 — 2,045
Shale as above and carbonaceous, green, fairly firm.... 88 — 2,133

	Thickness Ft.	Depth Ft.

Mohawkian series

Galena (Kimmswick) formation
Limestone, dolomitic at top, buff to light brown, fine-grained 19 — 2,152
Limestone, dolomitic, buff to light brown, coarse-grained, fossiliferous......... 101 — 2,253

	Thickness Ft. In.	Depth Ft. In.

2. *Standard Oil Company test boring, NE corner sec. 9, T. 10 N., R. 6 W. (Shaw Point Twp.)*[b]

Elevation 598 feet

Pleistocene system
Clay .... 6 — 6
Sand and gravel .... 3 — 9
Gravel and boulders .... 11 — 20
"Hardpan" (till?) ...... 8 — 28
Sand and gravel .... 12 — 40

Pennsylvanian system
Shale, blue .... 22— 6 — 62— 6
Limestone........ 1— 6 — 64
Shale, blue, sticky .... 7 — 71
Shale, black .... 3 — 74
Shale, gray, sticky .... 6 — 80
Limestone, brownish, crystalline, in concretionary beds up to 2 feet thick, in calcareous shale .... 10 — 90
Shale, limy, light blue gray, soft .... 12 — 102
Limestone, argillaceous ... 6— 6 — 108— 6
Shale, black .... 8 — 109— 2
Shale, light blue gray, laminated........... 12—10 — 122
Shale, slightly micaceous, carbonaceous, dark gray, with hard bands and plant impressions .... 13— 3 — 135— 3
Coal, very sooty ...... 7 — 135—10
Underclay, with root impressions .... 1— 2 — 137
Shale, dark .... 2 — 139
Sandstone or siltstone, slightly micaceous, gray, with limestone streaks and concretions 13 — 152
Siltstone or sandy shale, micaceous, greenish gray ... 32 — 184
Shale, bluish gray, laminated, fossiliferous in upper part .. 25— 6 — 209— 6
Shale, silty, calcareous, carbonaceous, dark gray .... 6 — 210
Shale, limy, greenish gray, laminated in lower part ... 4 — 214
Shale, silty, micaceous, greenish gray, laminated in upper part, dark gray at base ... 14 — 228
Clay, unctuous, slightly brownish .... 3 — 231
Shale, limy, greenish .... 8 — 239
Shale, sandy, micaceous, light gray, with clay beds 1 inch thick .... 1— 6 — 240— 6

[b]Includes data from a core study by G. H. Cady.

	Thickness Ft. In.	Depth Ft. In.
Shale, sandy, with limy streaks and concretions	1— 6	242
Shale, silty, light gray, micaceous in lower part, limy streaks and concretions, especially at base	8	250
Shale, gray, with streaks and thin beds of sand, limestone, and clay	8— 6	258— 6
Clay, with carbonaceous streaks; coaly streak at base	1— 6	260
Shale, clayey, greenish gray, with thin limestone bed at 267 feet	11	271
Coal, good quality	2— 2	273— 2
Shale, greenish, clayey at top, limestone streak at middle	4—10	278
Limestone, white, earthy, chalky, with crystalline quartz	6— 6	284— 6
Shale, calcareous, greenish	2— 2	286— 8
Limestone, argillaceous, white, fossiliferous	9	287— 5
Shale, limy, gray	7	288
Shale, calcareous, grayish green, hard	2— 6	290— 6
Limestone, argillaceous, dense, nodular	3— 6	294
Shale, dark	6	294— 6
Limestone	6	295
Shale, dark	10	295—10
Coal (Herrin No. 6)	6— 2	302
Underclay	10	302—10
Shale, more or less clayey, calcareous, dark greenish bluish gray to black, soft to hard, with limestone beds	21— 2	323
Shale, black, hard, laminated	2	325
Shale, sandy, greenish gray, hard	17	342
Sandstone, shaly, fine-grained, dense, hard	12	354
Shale, sandy, grayish green, massive	8	362
Shale, silty, bluish gray to dark gray, tough	33— 8	395— 8
Coal	2— 9	398— 5
Shale, sandy	1— 3	399— 8
Coal	8	400— 4
Shale, sandy, somewhat carbonaceous, bluish gray, hard	14— 8	415
Shale, bluish gray, laminated, tough	23	438
Shale, black, hard, laminated	2— 2	440— 2
Coal (Colchester No. 2), "bony" and shale, black	3— 4	443— 6
Underclay, sandy, gray, with organic partings and Stigmaria impressions	4— 6	448
Limestone, argillaceous, straw-colored, hard	1	449
Shale, micaceous, gray	2	451
Shale, black ("bony" coal?)	4	451— 4
Coal	8	452
Shale, black	1	453
Limestone, dark gray, dense, concretionary, with partings of shale, silty, gray	4	457
Shale, clayey, gray, soft	2	459

	Thickness Ft. In.	Depth Ft. In.
Clay, hard	2	461
Shale, sandy, micaceous, gray	14	475
Shale, micaceous, bituminous, bluish gray, "sticky"	2	477
Shale, sandy, micaceous, dark gray to black, laminated in upper part, carbonaceous or bituminous in lower part, with beds of sandstone, dark gray to black	28	505
Sandstone, white, with coaly or gray shale partings	4	509
Shale, silty, micaceous, gray, hard, massive	22— 9	531— 9
Shale, black	2	533— 9
Coal	2— 7	536— 4
Underclay, hard	8	537
Shale, calcareous, gray, hard, massive	4	541
Shale, calcareous, carbonaceous, black, fossiliferous	15	556
Shale, black, "sticky"	9	565
Shale, sandy, and sandstone, calcareous, carbonaceous, black	3	568
Limestone, argillaceous, dark	5	573
Shale, sandy	1	574
Limestone	1	575
Shale, silty, micaceous, dark gray, carbonaceous in lower 3 feet with half an inch of coal	6	581
Sandstone, argillaceous, fine-grained, white to light gray, with beds of purer sandstone and shale, carbonaceous and with thin streak of coal 3 feet above base	23— 6	604— 6
Shale, brownish gray to black	16— 6	621
Sandstone, coarse-grained	7	628

Mississippian system
Chester series

	Thickness Ft. In.	Depth Ft. In.
Shale, green, with streaks and nodules of limestone; thin beds of white calcareous sandstone in basal 3 feet	26	654

Iowa series
Meramec group
St. Louis formation

	Thickness Ft. In.	Depth Ft. In.
Limestone, crystalline, gray to white	41	695

3. *Fred Mudgett—Goebelt No. 8 well, center NW ¼ SW ¼ sec. 20, T. 10 N., R. 7. W. (Carlinville Twp.)*[e]

Elevation 611 feet

	Thickness Ft.	Depth Ft.
Pleistocene system		
Soil and clay	79	79
Pennsylvanian system		
Lime, hard	3	82
Shale, gray	8	90
Sandstone, micaceous, carbonaceous, slightly calcareous, light gray, very fine- to fine-grained	30	120

[e]Principally a sample study by Paul Herbert, Jr.

	Thickness Ft.	Depth Ft.
Shale, silty, gray	18	138
Limestone, silty, argillaceous, dark gray to buff mottled, very fine- to coarse-grained, fossiliferous	3	141
Sandstone, silty, micaceous, light gray, very fine- to fine-grained; sideritic nodules	24	165
Coal	3	168
Shale, silty, micaceous, light gray to white; many limestone and sideritic nodules	17	185
Shale, greenish gray, dense	7	192
Limestone, very light buff, extra fine-grained, dense	8	200
Shale, gray to buff, with limestone nodules, buff	12	212
Limestone, buff, extra fine-grained, dense	4	216
Shale, silty, dark gray, weak	3	219
Limestone, very pyritic, gray, very fine-grained, dense	4	223
Shale, gray to black, coally	2	225
Coal (Herrin No. 6)	4	229
Shale, silty, gray, weak, with buff to gray limestone nodules	11	240
Limestone, either light gray or silty, brown to black, all extra fine-grained, dense	7	247
Shale	18	265
Limestone	2	267
Shale	8	275
Sandstone, micaceous, very light gray, very fine- to fine-grained, sideritic spheres	15	290
Sandstone, same, slightly carbonaceous	15	305
Shale, silty, micaceous, dark gray, with interbedded siltstone	35	340
Coal	4	344
Shale, silty, white to light gray	7	351
Limestone, silty, partly pyritic, white to gray mottled, very fine- to medium-grained, partly fossiliferous	9	360
Shale, silty, very finely micaceous, white to gray, weak; dark in lower 5 feet	40	400
Coal, shiny, black	6	406
Shale, silty, micaceous, carbonaceous, dark gray and brown	4	410
Sandstone, silty, partly carbonaceous, white, very fine-grained	12	422
Shale, silty, micaceous, very light gray, weak, some sideritic nodules	15	437
Shale, silty, gray, flaky	8	445
Shale, green	5	450
Sandstone, very pyritic, fine-grained	7	457
Sandstone, buff, very fine-grained, incoherent, oil-stained	15	472

	Thickness Ft. In.	Depth Ft. In.

4. *Greenridge Coal Company, shaft No. 1, NE ¼ NW ¼ SW ¼ sec. 5, T. 11 N., R. 6. W. (Nilwood Township)*

Elevation 674 feet

Pleistocene system

	Thickness Ft. In.	Depth Ft. In.
Recent and Wisconsin stages		
Soil	3	3
Illinoian stage		
Clay, yellow	13	16
"Hardpan"	21	37
Pennsylvanian system		
Shale, blue	33	70
Shale, fossiliferous	3— 6	73— 6
Coal and shale mixed	12	85— 6
Shale, blue, with sandstone bands	13	98— 6
Shale, blue	3	101 6
Limestone	8	109— 6
Shale, blue and black	5	114— 6
Limestone	2	116— 6
Shale, dark	7	123— 6
Limestone, with partings	17	140— 6
Sandstone	30	170— 6
Shale, sand	11	181— 6
Shale, dark	2	183— 6
Coal	1	184— 6
Shale, blue	3— 9	188— 3
Sandstone, shaly with limestone partings	15	203— 3
Shale, sandy	10	213— 3
Shale, dark blue	14	227— 3
Shale, blue	8	235— 3
Shale, dark blue	23	258— 3
Shale, dark	4	262— 3
Coal	1	263— 3
Shale	3	266— 3
Shale, sandy	12	278— 3
Shale, dark	6	284— 3
Sandstone, shaly	12	296— 3
Shale, sandy	6	302— 3
Shale, with limestone bands	10	312— 3
Coal	1	313— 3
Shale	10	323— 3
Shale, limestone	15	338— 3
Shale, light	2	340— 3
Shale, blue, with limestone bands	11	351— 3
Coal (Herrin No. 6)	6— 9	358

5. *Standard Oil Company mine shaft No. 2, SE ¼ SW ¼ SW ¼ sec. 29, T. 11 N., R. 6 W. (Nilwood Twp.)*

Elevation 637 feet

Pleistocene system

	Thickness Ft. In.	Depth Ft. In.
Recent and Wisconsin stages		
Soil	2— 6	2— 6
Illinoian stage		
Clay, yellow	15— 6	18
"Hardpan"	12— 5	30— 5
Sand	13— 3	43— 8
Clay, sandy	15— 4	59
Clay, gravelly, hard	11	70
Clay, sandy	40	110
Clay, gravelly	3	113
Sand, with clay streaks	15— 6	128— 6
Clay, gravelly, and boulder	10— 6	139
Clay, sandy	13— 9	152— 9
Sand, fine-grained; contained piece of wood	20	172— 9
Gravel	9	173— 6
Pennsylvanian system		
Shale, blue	27— 6	201
Shale, dark	11	212
Shale, blue, tough	18	230
Shale, blue	27	257

	Thickness Ft. In.	Depth Ft. In.
Shale, dark	5	262
Underclay	3	265
Shale, dark	3— 6	268— 6
Shale, red	3	271— 6
Shale, limy	1— 6	273
Limestone, white	2	275
Shale, sandy	9— 4	284— 4
Shale, limy, concretionary	4— 5	288— 9
Limestone	2— 9	291— 6
Shale, clayey	2—11	294— 5
Coal	8	295— 1
Underclay	1— 7	296— 8
Limestone	4	297
Shale, blue	2— 6	299— 6
Limestone	2— 6	302
Shale, gray	4	306
Shale, blue	5— 6	311— 6
Limestone	1	312— 6
Shale, clayey	1— 2	313— 8
Shale, dark	1	314— 8
Limestone	6	315— 2
Shale, black	4— 4	319— 6
Coal (No. 6 Herrin)	6—11	326— 5
Underclay	2— 5	328—10
Limestone	5—11	334— 9
Limestone and shale	1— 3	336
Shale, limy	4— 6	340— 6
Shale	2— 9	343— 3
Limestone	1— 9	345
Shale	3— 4	348— 4
Limestone, shaly	2	350— 4
Shale, gray	3— 2	353— 6
Slate, black, laminated, hard	3	356— 6
Coal	6	357
Underclay	5	362
Sandstone	12	374
Shale, sandy, dark	1	375
Sandstone	6	381
Sandstone, shaly	19	400

6. Adams and Lagers—Bristow No. 1 well, SE ¼ SE ¼ NE ¼ sec. 7, T. 11 N., R. 7 W. (South Otter Twp.)[d]

Elevation 639 feet

	Thickness Ft.	Depth Ft.
Pleistocene system		
Clay, red, with gravel	45	45
Clay and gravel, blue	50	95
Sand and gravel, with blue clay	17	112
Clay, blue	35	147
Pennsylvanian system		
Limestone, sandy, hard	7	154
Shale, black	26	180
Limestone	5	185
Shale, calcareous, black, brittle, fossiliferous	4	189
Coal, shaly	2	191
Sandstone, silty, micaceous, light gray, fine-grained, siderite spherules	17	208
Dolomite, light gray, fine-grained	12	220
Siltstone, calcareous, light greenish gray	5	225
Dolomite, silty, light gray, very fine-grained; limestone, conglomerate of gray and buff fragments	5	230
Shale, black, tough	4	234
Coal, dull to shiny	6	240
Limestone, black, fine-grained, dense	5	245
Shale, silty, black, tough	5	250
Sandstone, calcareous, micaceous, gray, fine; chert, brown, dense	25	280
Shale, silty, gray, firm	10	290
Limestone, silty, greenish gray, fine-grained	15	305
Sandstone, slightly calcareous, micaceous, light gray to brown; some siltstone and chert	15	320
Shale, black, tough	3	323
Coal, dull	4	327
Sandstone, slightly calcareous, micaceous, carbonaceous at top, light gray to gray, fine-grained	23	350
Shale, silty, micaceous, gray, firm	20	370
Shale, black, tough; trace of shiny coal	5	375
Limestone, gray, some buff mottled, fine-grained	20	395
Siltstone, grading to some sandstone, micaceous, light gray	10	405
Shale, silty, micaceous, gray brown	10	415
Shale, black, tough	5	420
Siltstone, micaceous, light gray, very fine-grained, sandy toward base	15	435
Sandstone, slightly carbonaceous, light gray, fine-grained, well sorted, secondarily enlarged	5	440
Shale, micaceous, gray, firm	5	445
Siltstone, brown, dense; chert, brown, dense; a little coal	5	450
Siltstone, micaceous, light gray	5	455
Shale, silty, micaceous, brown gray, tough	5	460
Siltstone, micaceous, gray	10	470
Sandstone, micaceous, white, fine-grained, with siderite spherules; shaly, carbonaceous, black, in middle	15	485
Siltstone, micaceous, gray, some very fine-grained sand	30	515
Sandstone, micaceous, white, fine-grained, well sorted	13	528
Siltstone, brown to gray; a little coal at top	7	535
Shale, silty, carbonaceous, gray	5	540
Siltstone, gray to brown, dense	10	550
Sandstone, brown, medium- to fine-grained, mostly siderite spherules; pyritic at base	14	564
Mississippian system		
Iowa series		
Meramec group		
Ste. Genevieve formation		
Limestone, sandy, light gray, fine-grained	12	576
St. Louis formation		
Limestone, white to very light gray, very fine-grained, some calcite; silty in middle	48	624

[d]In part, sample study by Paul Herbert, Jr.

	Thick-ness Ft.	Depth Ft.
Limestone, light gray, very fine-grained, with chert, white to gray, dense; silty at top, dolomite in middle, some conglomerate at bottom	41	665
Dolomite, light gray, very fine-grained, crystalline	15	680
Limestone, light gray buff, lithographic, medium- to coarse grained near top	33	713
Limestone, silty, dolomitic in middle, light gray to light brown, fine- to coarse-grained at top to lithographic at bottom; many calcite fragments .	41	754
Salem formation		
Dolomite, light buff to light brown, some gray, very fine- to fine-grained, crystalline; much chert, white to buff, dense. . .	14	768
Limestone, some dolomitic, some silty, gray to buff, mottled, oolitic, coarse- to fine-grained, fossiliferous; glauconitic in lower part.	82	850
Dolomite, light brownish gray, very fine-grained, crystalline, vesicular, slightly glauconitic, some calcite	16	866
Osage group		
Warsaw formation		
Shale, very silty, calcareous, gray, firm	15	881
Limestone, more or less dolomitic, silty, light gray to gray, fine- to coarse-grained, some green shale mottling; cherty at top	39	920
Shale, silty, calcareous, gray, fossiliferous; some coarse-grained, glauconitic; much milky quartz	20	940
Limestone, gray to buff, fine- to coarse-grained; contains many bryozoa and crinoid fragments	30	970
Shale, silty, micaceous, gray, contains bryozoa	20	990
Keokuk-Burlington formations		
Dolomite, very silty, slightly glauconitic, light gray; much chert, light gray with white stringers	15	1,005
Limestone, white to light buff, much chert as above.	20	1,025
Limestone, light blue gray, hard, softer in middle	50	1,075
Limestone, white to bluish gray, soft	93	1,168
Fern Glen formation		
Limestone, sandy, and "red rock"	22	1,190
Limestone, white to light buff, fine- to coarse-grained; some chert, white	34	1,224
Kinderhook group		
Hannibal formation		
Maple Mill and Hamburg members		
Shale, silty, gray	6	1,230

	Thick-ness Ft.	Depth Ft.
Siltstone, light gray; some limestone, light buff, fine-grained .	15	1,245
Shale, gray.	5	1,250
Siltstone, calcareous, light gray, becoming noncalcareous and cherty in lower half . . .	65	1,315
Siltstone, some very fine sand, slightly calcareous, very light gray.	10	1,325
Grassy Creek formation		
Shale, silty, micaceous, dark gray to brown; contains spores	35	1,360
Shale, very dark brown, some pyritic; contains spores. . . .	60	1,420
Shale, silty, light gray to gray, pyritic; contains spores . . .	10	1,430
Devonian system		
Cedar Valley formation		
Chert, very light buff to light gray, dense.	11	1,441
Sandstone, very dolomitic, gray, very fine-grained to silty	5	1,446
Wapsipinicon formation		
Dolomite, light brownish gray, very fine-grained	6	1,452
Limestone, very fine-grained to sublithographic, scattered rounded sand grains	18	1,470
Silurian system		
Limestone, silty, micaceous, light gray, very fine-grained; contains scattered crinoids . .	5	1,475
Limestone, slightly dolomitic, silty, white, fine-grained . . .	12	1,487

	Thick-ness Ft. In.	Depth Ft. In.

7. *Northwestern Macoupin Coal Company contract No. 1 test drilling, SW corner NE 1/4 sec. 4, T. 11 N., R. 8 W. (South Palmyra Twp.)*

Elevation 659 feet

	Thickness Ft. In.	Depth Ft. In.
Pleistocene system		
Recent and Wisconsin stages		
Soil	2	2
Illinoian stage		
Clay	16	18
Clay, sandy	17	35
Clay, gravelly	3	38
Clay	2	40
Clay, sandy	6	46
Gravel	1	47
Pennsylvanian system		
Limestone, blue	2— 6	49— 6
Shale, blue and yellow . . .	7— 6	57
Sandstone, shale partings . .	10	67
Shale, sandy, blue	10	77
Shale, blue	6— 6	83— 6
Coal	4	83—10
Shale, clayey, very soft . . .	9	92—10
Shale, blue	5— 2	98
Shale, sandy, blue	25	123
Shale, dark blue	19— 4	142— 4
Limestone, blue	4—10	147— 2
Shale, dark	5— 6	152— 8
Shale, limy	5— 4	158

	Thick-ness Ft. In.	Depth Ft. In.
Shale, sandy, blue, with limestone bands	19— 3	177— 3
Shale, black	2— 8	179—11
Shale, fossiliferous	3	180— 2
Coal	5	180— 7
Shale, blue, soft	2— 5	183
Shale, clayey	8	191
Shale, sandy	9	200
Shale, light blue, with limestone bands	9	209
Limestone	3	212
Shale, soft, blue	5	217
Sandstone	5— 5	222— 5
Limestone	10	223— 3
Shale, dark	3— 9	227
Shale, limy	6	233
Limestone	2— 8	235— 8
Shale, gray, soft	4— 4	240
Shale, black	1	241
Coal	10	241—10
Shale	1	241—11
Coal (Herrin No. 6), with ½-inch sulfur band	4— 6	246— 5
Underclay	1— 7	248
Shale, blue with limestone concretion	8	256
Shale, gray, soft	8— 4	264— 4
Shale, black	6	264—10
Shale, gray, soft	9— 2	274
Shale, blue, soft	10— 6	284— 6
Shale, sandy, blue	5— 6	290
Sandstone	32	322
Coal	1— 6	323— 6
Shale, sandy, dark	24— 6	348
Shale, dark blue	15— 9	363— 9
Shale, black	2— 3	366
Shale, fossiliferous	1	366— 1
Coal	11	367
Coal, bony	1	368
Coal	10	368—10
Shale, clayey	3— 2	372
Limestone	8	380
Shale, soft, blue	24	404
Shale, black	4	404— 4
Coal, bony	1— 8	406
Underclay	2	408
Shale, soft, gray	12	420
Shale, dark blue	6	426
Shale, black	7	433
Shale, clayey	4	437
Shale, gray	2	439
Shale, red and blue	3	442
Conglomerate and sandstone	3	445
Shale, sandy	2	447
Shale, black	24	471
Shale, gray	6	477
Shale, sandy	40	517
Conglomerate	4	521
Mississippian system		
St. Louis and Salem formations		
Limestone	257	778
Warsaw formation		
Shale, limy	11	789
Shale, sandy	10	799
Shale, hard, laminated, gray	37	836
Limestone	2	838
Shale, gray	2	840
Limestone	2	842

	Thick-ness Ft. In.	Depth Ft. In.
Shale, gray	5	847
Shale, hard, laminated	3	850
Keokuk formation		
Limestone	18	868
Limestone, crystalline	7	875

8. *Phillips Petroleum Company—Giller No. 1 well, NW ¼ NE ¼ NW ¼ sec. 15, T. 11 N., R. 8 W. (South Palmyra Twp.)* [e]

Elevation 578 feet

	Thick-ness Ft.	Depth Ft.
No record	40	40
Pennsylvanian system		
Shale, micaceous, gray	15	55
Limestone, gray to brownish gray, fine-grained, dense	5	60
Sandstone, micaceous, light gray, fine-grained	12	72
Shale, silty, gray	6	78
Limestone, shaly, dark gray	2	80
Shale, black, brittle; little coal	2	82
Shale, gray	3	85
Sandstone, micaceous, light gray, fine-grained	18	103
Shale, silty, gray	5	108
Shale, black	2	110
Shale, silty, gray	2	112
Shale, black, brittle; a little coal	2	114
Limestone, light gray buff, some black, fine-grained, some fossiliferous; inter-bedded with shale	32	146
Shale, black to dark gray; a little coal (Herrin No. 6) below	2	148
Limestone, shaly, gray, fine-grained, dense	12	160
Dolomite, shaly, gray, fine-grained; many large siderite spherules, with pyrite	10	170
Sandstone, calcareous, micaceous, fine- to very fine-grained, light gray; many siderite spherules	30	200
Shale, silty, gray	8	208
Shale, micaceous, black	2	210
Shale, silty, sandy, gray, sideritic at top	15	225
Sandstone, silty, micaceous, carbonaceous, slightly calcareous, light gray, fine-grained	15	240
Shale, sandy, silty, micaceous, gray to brown, some carbonaceous	24	264
Shale, black, brittle	2	266
Shale, brown, sideritic, brittle	4	270
Limestone, light gray to brown, fine-grained	12	282
Shale, slightly sandy, gray	8	290
Shale, calcareous, brownish-gray, "greasy," tough	8	298
Shale, calcareous, gray and red	4	302
Shale, limy, light gray, with brown sideritic spherules	8	310
Shale, light gray, some black carbonaceous, a few lime streaks	10	320

[e]In part, sample study by Paul Herbert, Jr.

	Thick-ness Ft.	Depth Ft.
Shale, silty, sandy at top, micaceous, gray	20	340
Shale, dark gray to brownish gray, sideritic, dense, "greasy"	18	358
Shale, black	6	364
Sandstone, black to gray, fine-grained	3	367
Limestone, silty, carbonaceous, brownish gray, crinoidal	3	370
Shale, silty, sandy, micaceous, slightly carbonaceous, gray	40	410
Shale, carbonaceous, black	2	412
Sandstone, medium- to some fine- and coarse-grained, some rounded coarse grains	33	448
Mississippian system		
Iowa series		
Meramec group		
St. Louis formation		
Limestone, light buff, very fine-grained	22	470
Dolomite, gray brown to light buff, fine-grained, crystalline	28	498
Limestone, light gray to buff, very fine-grained to lithographic, dense	20	518
Limestone, light buff, fine- to very fine-grained	15	533
Limestone, light buff to light brown, fine- to medium-grained	27	560
Salem formation		
Dolomite, cherty, silty, with siderite spherules at top, light gray to brown, finely crystalline; chert, white to buff mottled	25	585
Limestone, gray buff, medium- to fine-grained; chert, gray to buff to white mottled	10	595
Dolomite, cherty at bottom, some brown-orange specks, very finely crystalline	15	610
Limestone, dolomitic at bottom, buff to gray mottled, fine- to coarse-grained, fossiliferous, some *Endothyra*	23	633
Dolomite, buff, finely crystalline, interbedded with limestone, shaly, gray, fine- to coarse-grained, fossiliferous, and shale, gray	75	708
Osage group		
Warsaw formation		
Sandstone, silty, very dolomitic, glauconitic, light gray, very fine-grained	7	715
Limestone, dolomitic, gray to buff to argillaceous, pale green, coarse-grained, partly fossiliferous	35	750
Shale, dolomitic, silty, micaceous, light gray, with chert, white to gray, in bottom 25 feet	60	810
Keokuk and Burlington formations		
Limestone, slightly dolomitic, cherty, white, fine- to coarse-grained; chert, white, dense	50	860

	Thick-ness Ft.	Depth Ft.
Limestone, cherty, white, fine- to medium-grained; chert, white, dull	40	900
Limestone, dolomitic, very cherty, white to light buff, fine-grained, partly crystalline	78	978
Fern Glen formation		
Siltstone, pale green and white, interlayered with light green shale	7	985
Limestone, cherty, white	5	990
Siltstone, pale green	5	995
Limestone, cherty, dolomitic, white to some pink and green, fine-grained; chert, white to pink	10	1,005
Shale, sandy, pale green	5	1,010
Limestone, dolomitic, slightly silty, slightly cherty, white, very fine- to some coarse-grained	37	1,047
Kinderhook group		
Hannibal formation		
Maple Mill member		
Siltstone, calcareous, light gray to pale greenish gray; some very silty limestone	23	1,070
Hamburg member		
Siltstone, calcareous, some very fine sand, light gray	60	1,130
Limestone, silty, very oolitic, gray buff, fine-grained; shaly, greenish at bottom	15	1,145
Grassy Creek formation		
Shale, silty, light brown, sporiferous	25	1,170
Shale, slightly micaceous, dark brown, sporiferous	66	1,236
Sandstone, very pyritic	1	1,237
Devonian system		
Wapsipinicon formation		
Dolomite, light brown, fine-grained, crystalline, cherty at top, sandy at bottom	18	1,255
Limestone, very sandy, buff to gray, very fine-grained, some chert, white	10	1,265
Limestone, slightly sandy, cherty, light buff, fine-grained	10	1,275
Silurian system		
Niagaran series		
Dolomite, silty, very light greenish gray, very fine- to fine-grained, crystalline	35	1,310
Limestone, slightly dolomitic, white, fine-grained	60	1,370
Limestone, dolomitic, white to pink, fine-grained to some coarse pink crinoids	80	1,450
Alexandrian series		
Kankakee formation		
Limestone, slightly dolomitic, cherty, glauconitic, light gray buff to some pale greenish, fine-grained	23	1,473
Edgewood formation		
Dolomite, slightly argillaceous, light brown, fine-grained, crystalline	15	1,488

	Thick-ness Ft.	Depth Ft.
Ordovician system		
Maquoketa formation		
Shale	2	1,490
Limestone, dolomitic, oolitic, buff	6	1,496
Shale, hard	7	1,503
Limestone, light gray	4	1,507
Dolomite, buff	7	1,514
Shale, brown	3	1,517
Dolomite, buff	8	1,525
Limestone, dolomitic, light greenish gray	5	1,530
Shale, sandy, laminated	20	1,550
Limestone, dolomitic, buff	12	1,562
Shale, sandy, green gray	16	1,578
Limestone, shaly, gray, fossiliferous	17	1,595
Shale, calcareous, light brown	20	1,615
Limestone, shaly, green gray	25	1,640
Dolomite, tan	7	1,647
Limestone, white, crystalline, trace of chert	16	1,663
Shale, light brown and green gray, laminated	24	1,687
Kimmswick formation		
Limestone, slightly dolomitic, light buff to some gray, brown orange specks and partings, fine- to coarse-grained	116	1,803
Decorah formation		
Limestone, gray, very fine-grained, dense; some shale, green-gray	7	1,810
Dolomite, buff, fine- to medium-grained	10	1,820
Plattin formation		
Limestone, cherty, light gray to gray, very fine- grained, dense	8	1,828

	Thick-ness Ft. In.	Depth Ft. In.

9. *Virden Mining Company, south shaft, NW ¼ SW ¼ SE ¼ sec. 9, T. 12 N., R. 6 W. (Virden Twp.)*

Elevation 661 feet

	Thick-ness Ft. In.	Depth Ft. In.
Pleistocene system		
Illinoian stage		
Drift clay	20	20
Pennsylvanian system		
Sandstone	5	25
Shale, bituminous	5	25— 5
Coal	2	25— 7
Underclay	5	30— 7
Shale, bituminous	4— 6	35— 1
Coal	6	35— 7
Underclay or clayey shale	6	41— 7
Limestone, gray, hard	7— 9	49— 4
Shale, bituminous	1— 4	50— 8
Shale, argillaceous	5— 6	56— 2
Limestone, compact	7	63— 2
Shale, bituminous, and coal	1— 3	64— 5
Shale, clayey	6	70— 5
Limestone	9	71— 2
Shale, sandy, and sandstone	63	134— 2
Limestone, soft, or shale, calcareous	1— 4	135— 6

	Thick-ness Ft. In.	Depth Ft. In.
Shale, bituminous	3—10	139— 4
Coal	10	140— 2
Sandstone and sandy shale	72	212— 2
Shales, with "ironstone"	3	215— 2
Sandstone, calcareous?, hard	8	223— 2
Shale, clayey, blue	4	227— 2
Shales, variegated (with coal?)	22— 6	249— 8
Shale, sandy	26	275— 8
Shale, bituminous, soft	1— 6	277— 2
Limestone	3	280— 2
Shale, bituminous	2— 6	282— 8
Coal	2— 9	285— 5
Underclay	2	287— 5
Sandstone	4	291— 5
Coal	1— 6	292—11
Underclay	2	294—11
Sandstone and shale	10	304—11
Limestone	7	311—11
Shale, bituminous	6	312— 5
Coal (Herrin No. 6)	7— 8	320— 1

10. *O. G. Hayes—Alderson No. 1 well, SE ¼ SE ¼ NE ¼ sec. 17, T. 12 N., R. 7 W. (North Otter Twp.)* [f]

Elevation 665 feet

	Thickness	Depth
Pleistocene system		
Surface	2	2
Clay, yellow	18	20
Clay, sandy, blue	6	26
Clay, sandy, blue, soft	59	85
Sand, medium- to coarse-grained, angular; some gravel	10	95
Pennsylvanian system		
Sandstone, slightly calcareous, micaceous, light gray, fine-grained	64	159
Limestone, partly silty, gray to buff mottled, very fine- to coarse-grained, dense	6— 6	165— 6
Shale, silty, black; coal, shiny, black	5— 6	171
Sandstone, slightly micaceous, light gray, fine-grained	9	180
Shale, blue and gray	20	200
Limestone, very silty, light gray to light green gray, very fine-grained, some coarse crinoid stems	3— 6	203—6
Shale, sandy, gray and blue	8— 6	212
Shale, light gray, with streaks of limestone at bottom	15	227
Limestone, very silty, dolomitic, light buff, extra fine-grained, dense; coarse-grained and fossiliferous at base	12	239
Shale, black, hard, laminated, and coal	5	244
Shale, silty, gray	6	250
Limestone, brown, fine- to very fine-grained, crystalline, dense	5	255
Shale; many siderite and pyrite spherules	5	260

[f]In part, sample study by Paul Herbert, Jr.

	Thick-ness Ft.	Depth Ft.
Limestone, very light gray, fine- to very fine-grained; siderite spherules.	5	265
Sandstone, calcareous, partly micaceous, light gray, fine- to very fine-grained; some siderite spherules and dense siderite	40	305
Shale, silty, light gray to light brown; siderite, brown, dense.	15	320
Shale, silty, partly micaceous, black to dark gray, dull; some coal	10	330
Sandstone, micaceous, silty, carbonaceous, light gray, fine- to very fine-grained.	20	350
Shale, silty, finely carbonaceous, gray to brown gray .	15	365
Limestone, partly very silty and carbonaceous, gray to buff mottled, fine- to coarse-grained, fossiliferous	5	370
Shale, black, dull; some coal .	5	375
Limestone, light buff to brown to gray mottled, very fine- to medium-grained, fossiliferous; sandy at base	20	395
Shale, "greasy," gray. . . .	20	415
Shale, silty, sandy, carbonaceous, light brown gray, weak; siderite spherules	28	443
Shale, sandy, black green . .	7	450
Sandstone, partly argillaceous, white, fine- to medium-grained; some siderite cement and spherules	24	474
Shale, black, hard, laminated; siderite, brown, dense. . . .	6	480
Shale, "greasy," brown gray; siderite spherules, red brown, dense.	5	485
Shale, silty, gray, thinly bedded; some siderite, brown, dense.	45	530
Sandstone, white to brown, medium- to coarse-grained; much siderite cement. . . .	18	548
Shale, silty, very fine-grained, dark gray	2	550

Mississippian system
Chester series
Aux Vases (?) formation

	Thick-ness Ft.	Depth Ft.
Sandstone, calcareous, silty, slightly micaceous, partly argillaceous, very light gray to pale green gray, very fine-grained	13	563

Iowa series
Meramec group
Ste. Genevieve formation

	Thick-ness Ft.	Depth Ft.
Limestone, coarsely oolitic, sandy, white, very fine-grained	20	583
Limestone, very sandy, white to very light gray, fine- to very fine-grained. .	12	595

St. Louis formation

	Thick-ness Ft.	Depth Ft.
Dolomite, gray-buff, fine-grained, crystalline, partly vesicular	11	606

	Thick-ness Ft.	Depth Ft.
Limestone, white to very light buff, fine- to medium-grained, some lithographic.	10	616

	Thick-ness Ft. In.	Depth Ft. In.

11. *Test drilling, NE ¼ SW ¼ SW ¼ sec. 15, T. 12 N., R. 8 W. (North Palmyra Twp.)*

Elevation 685 feet

Pleistocene system
Recent and Wisconsin stages

	Thick-ness Ft. In.	Depth Ft. In.
Soil, black.	3	3

Illinoian stage

Clay, yellow.	6	9
Sand and gravel	15	24
Clay, yellow, and gravel . .	5	29
Gravel, bouldery.	2	31
Clay, yellow.	6	37

Pennsylvanian system

Shale, black and blue . . .	10	47
Coal	1	48
Shale, gray, soft	6	54
Shale, sandy.	5	59
Shale and limestone, sandy .	29	88
Sandstone.	18	106
Limestone.	3	109
Sandstone.	6	115
Shale, blue	1	116
Limestone.	2	118
Limestone, black.	4	122
Shale.	8	130
Coal	1	131
Shale, light gray	8	139
Shale, blue	15	154
Coal	2	156
Shale, blue, and coal . . .	1	157
Shale, blue	2— 6	159— 6
Limestone.	1— 6	161
Shale, limy	4	165
Shale, blue	9	174
Limestone.	3	177
Shale, red.	2	179
Shale, light gray	9	188
Shale, red	1	189
Limestone, very hard . . .	1	190
Shale, dark blue	1	191
Limestone, black.	7	198
Limestone.	5	203
Limestone, light gray . . .	2	205
Shale, black	2	207
Coal (Herrin No. 6) . . .	3	210
Shale, light gray	3	213
Limestone.	6	219
Shale, blue, soft, with limestone and sandstone . . .	10	229
Shale, blue	3	232
Shale, sandy, white. . . .	25	257
Shale, blue	36	293
Coal	1	294
Shale, blue	4	298
Sandstone, with bands of shale	7	305
Sandstone.	6	311
Sandstone, with shale. . .	5	316
Shale, sandy, blue	7	323
Shale, blue, with brown sand.	14	337
Coal, bony	2	339
Coal, good quality	2— 6	341— 6
Underclay.	1— 6	343
Limestone.	7	350

APPENDIX C — FOSSIL LISTS

PART I.—TABULATED LIST OF FOSSILS FROM PENNSYLVANIAN STRATA IN THE CARLINVILLE QUADRANGLE

Cyclothem:	Trivoli	Carlinville			Burroughs		Macoupin					Shoal Creek		
Stratum[1]:	a	b	c	d	e	e	f	g	h	h	i	j	k	k
Locality[2]:	1	2	3	4	5	6	7	6	8	7	9	10	11	10
Foraminifera														
Ammodiscus incertus	–	x	–	–	–	–	–	–	–	–	–	–	–	–
Textrataxis sp.	–	x	–	–	–	–	–	–	–	–	–	–	–	–
Tuberitina sp.	–	x	–	–	–	–	–	–	–	–	–	–	–	–
Fusulina sp.	–	–	x	–	–	–	–	–	–	–	–	–	–	–
Porifera														
Sponge fragments	–	–	–	–	–	–	–	–	–	–	x	–	–	–
Corals														
Lophophyllum profundum	–	–	–	–	–	–	–	–	–	–	–	–	x	–
L. profundum var. radicostum	–	–	–	–	–	–	–	–	–	–	–	–	x	–
Lophophyllum sp.	–	–	–	–	–	–	–	–	–	–	–	–	x	–
Crinoids														
Plates and stem fragments	–	–	–	–	–	–	–	–	–	x	–	–	–	–
Sea Urchins														
Echinoid spines	–	–	–	–	–	–	–	–	–	–	–	–	–	–
Bryozoa														
Fenestella sp.	–	–	–	–	x	–	–	–	–	–	–	–	–	–
Polypora sp.	–	–	x	–	–	–	–	–	–	–	–	–	–	–
Rhombopora lepidodendroides	–	–	–	–	–	–	–	–	x	x	–	–	–	–
Brachiopods														
Lingula carbonaria	x	–	–	x	–	–	–	–	–	–	–	–	–	–
Trigonoglossa nebrascensis	–	–	–	x	–	–	–	–	–	–	–	–	–	–
Orbiculoidea missourensis	–	–	–	x	–	–	–	–	x	–	–	–	–	–
Derbya crassa	–	–	–	–	–	–	x	–	–	x	–	–	–	–
Chonetes granulifer	–	–	–	–	x	–	–	x	–	x	–	–	x	–
Chonetes sp.	–	–	–	–	–	–	–	–	–	–	x	–	x	–
Juresania nebrascensis	–	–	–	–	x	–	x	–	–	–	–	–	–	–
Pustula pustulosa	–	–	–	–	–	–	–	–	–	–	x	–	–	–
Marginifera splendens	–	x	x	–	–	–	–	x	–	x	–	–	x	x
Marginifera wabashensis	–	–	–	–	–	–	–	x	–	–	–	–	x	–
Linoproductus prattenianus	–	–	–	–	–	–	–	–	–	x	–	–	–	–
Wellerella cf. osagensis	–	–	–	–	–	–	–	–	–	–	–	–	x	–
Wellerella tetrahedra	–	–	–	–	–	–	x	–	–	–	–	–	x	x
Dielasma bovidens	–	–	–	–	?	cf.	x	–	–	–	–	–	x	–
Dielasma sp.	–	–	–	–	–	–	–	–	–	–	–	–	x	–
Neospirifer cameratus	–	–	–	–	–	–	–	x	–	x	x	–	x	x
Neospirifer triplicatus	–	–	–	–	–	–	–	–	–	–	–	–	x	–
Punctospirifer kentuckyensis	–	–	–	–	–	–	–	–	–	–	x	–	–	x
Squamularia perplexa	–	–	–	–	–	–	–	–	–	x	x	–	x	–
Ambocoelia planoconvexa	–	–	–	–	–	–	–	–	–	x	x	–	x	–
Hustedia mormoni	–	–	–	–	–	–	–	–	–	–	–	–	x	–
Composita subtilita	–	–	x	–	x	–	x	–	–	–	x	–	x	x
Composita trilobita	–	–	–	–	?	–	–	–	–	–	–	–	–	–
Composita cf. elongata	–	–	–	–	–	–	–	–	–	–	–	–	cf.	–

[1]*Key to strata:*

a. Shale overlying No. 8 coal.
b. Shale interbedded with limestone strata.
c. Upper ledge of the limestone member.
d. Dark shale under the upper limestone ledge.
e. Limestone member.
f. Limestone underlying the coal.
g. Shale or clay under the black sheety shale.
h. Macoupin limestone member, lower part.
i. Macoupin limestone member, upper part.
j. Limestone near the base of the thin limestone bands, interbedded with shales.
k. Shoal Creek limestone member.

PART I.—Concluded

	Trivoli	Carlinville			Burroughs		Macoupin					Shoal Creek		
Cyclothem: Stratum[1]: Locality[2]:	a 1	b 2	c 3	d 4	e 5	e 6	f 7	g 6	h 8	h 7	i 9	j 10	k 11	k 10
Pelecypoda														
Leda bellestriata	–	–	–	–	–	–	–	–	–	x	–	–	cf.	–
Astartella vera	–	x	x	–	–	–	–	x	–	–	–	–	–	–
Astartella sp.	–	–	–	–	–	–	–	–	x	–	–	–	–	–
Myalina swallowi	–	–	–	–	–	–	–	–	x	–	–	–	–	–
Myalina sp.	–	–	–	–	?	–	–	–	x	–	–	–	–	–
Aviculopecten occidentalis	–	–	–	–	cf.	–	–	–	–	–	–	–	–	–
Gastropods														
Cyrtolites ? gillanus	–	–	–	–	–	–	–	–	–	–	–	–	cf.	–
Euphemus carbonarius	–	x	–	–	–	–	–	–	–	–	–	–	–	–
Gosseletina spironema	–	–	–	–	–	–	–	–	–	–	–	–	x	–
Yvania sp.	–	–	–	–	–	–	–	–	–	–	–	–	x	–
Porcellia sp.	–	–	–	–	–	–	–	–	–	–	–	–	x	–
Phanerotrema grayvillensis	–	–	–	–	–	–	–	–	–	x	–	–	–	–
Trepospira sphaerulata	–	x	–	–	–	–	–	–	–	–	–	–	–	–
Trepospira illinoisensis	–	x	–	–	–	–	–	–	–	–	–	–	–	–
Straparolus sp.	–	–	–	–	–	–	–	–	–	–	–	–	x	–
Schizostoma catelloides	–	–	–	–	–	–	–	–	x	x	–	–	–	–
Strophostylus sp.	–	–	–	–	–	–	–	–	–	–	–	–	–	?
Naticopsis ventricosa	–	–	x	–	–	–	x	–	–	–	–	–	x	–
Naticopsis sp.	–	–	–	–	–	–	–	–	–	–	–	–	x	–
Aclisina stevensana	–	–	–	–	–	–	–	–	–	–	–	x	–	–
Aclisina conditi	–	–	–	–	–	–	–	–	–	–	–	cf.	–	–
Aclisina swallowana	–	–	–	–	–	–	–	–	–	–	–	x	–	–
Sphaerodoma primogenia	–	x	–	–	–	–	–	–	–	–	–	–	–	–
Sphaerodoma sp.	–	–	–	–	–	–	–	–	–	–	–	x	–	–
Platyceras trigonalis	–	–	–	–	–	–	–	–	–	–	–	–	x	–
Nuculopsis ventricosa	–	x	–	–	–	–	–	–	–	–	–	–	–	–
Cephalopods														
Pseudorthoceras knoxense	–	–	–	–	–	–	–	–	–	x	–	–	–	–
Pseudorthoceras sp.	–	–	–	–	–	–	–	–	–	x	–	–	–	–
Metacoceras sp.	–	–	–	–	–	–	–	–	–	x	–	–	x	–
Nautilus sp.	–	–	–	–	–	–	–	–	–	–	–	–	x	–
Trilobites														
Phillipsia sangamonensis	–	–	–	–	x	–	–	–	–	–	–	–	–	–
Ostracods														
Primitia sp.	–	–	–	–	–	–	–	–	–	–	–	x	–	–
Jonesina arcuata	–	–	–	–	–	–	–	–	–	–	–	x	–	–
Kirbya sp.	–	x	–	–	–	–	–	–	–	–	–	–	–	–
Bairdia ardmorensis	–	x	–	–	–	–	–	–	–	–	–	–	–	–
Bairdia elongata	–	cf.	–	–	–	–	–	–	–	–	–	–	–	–
Bairdia sp.	–	x	–	–	–	–	–	–	–	–	–	–	–	–
Vertebrates														
Fish teeth	–	–	–	–	–	–	–	–	–	–	–	x	–	–

[2]*Key to localities:*

1. NE ¼ SW ¼ sec. 10, T. 11 N., R. 8 W. (South Palmyra Twp.) (geologic section 3).
2. SE ¼ SW ¼ sec. 23, T. 12 N., R. 8 W. (North Palmyra Twp.) (geologic section 6).
3. SE ¼ NE ¼ sec. 34, T. 12 N., R. 8 W. (North Palmyra Twp.) (geologic section 8).
4. SW ¼ NW ¼ sec. 10, T. 11 N., R. 8 W., (South Palmyra Twp.) (geologic section 9).
5. NE ¼ sec. 34, T. 10 N., R. 7 W. (Carlinville Twp.) (geologic section 12).
6. NE ¼ NW ¼ sec. 2, T. 9 N., R. 7 W. (Brushy Mound Twp.) (geologic section 19).
7. NW ¼ NE ¼ sec. 25, T. 10 N., R. 7 W. (Carlinville Twp.) (geologic section 23).
8. SW ¼ NE ¼ sec. 3, T. 9 N., R. 7 W. (Brushy Mound Twp.)
9. W ½ sec. 2, T. 9 N., R. 7 W. (Brushy Mound Twp.) (geologic section 25).
10. SW ¼ SE ¼ sec. 35, T. 10 N., R. 7 W. (Carlinville Twp.) (geologic section 19).
11. NW ¼ sec. 36, T. 10 N., R. 7 W. (Carlinville Twp.) (geologic section 35).

APPENDIX C

PART II.—TABULATED LIST OF FOSSILS FROM PLEISTOCENE DEPOSITS IN THE CARLINVILLE QUADRANGLE

Localities[1]	Yarmouth						Sangamon	
	a	b	c	d	e	f	g	h
Pelecypods								
Pisidium	x	x	x	–	–	x	–	–
Gastropods								
Carychium exiguum	x	–	–	–	–	–	–	–
Carychium exile	x	–	–	–	–	x	–	–
Physa integra	–	–	–	–	–	–	x	–
Physa walkeri	–	–	–	–	–	–	x	–
Physa sp.	–	–	–	–	–	–	–	x
Fossaria dalli	x	–	–	–	–	x	–	–
Fossaria obrussa decampi	x	x	x	–	–	–	–	–
Fossaria parva tazewelliana	x	–	–	–	–	x	–	–
Pupilla muscorum	x	–	–	–	x	–	–	–
Pupilla muscorum unidentata	x	–	–	–	–	–	–	–
Vertigo hannai	x	–	–	–	x	–	–	–
Vertigo loessensis	x	–	x	–	x	x	–	–
Vertigo morsei	x	–	x	–	–	x	–	–
Vertigo ovata	x	–	–	–	–	–	–	–
Helisoma antrosum striatum	–	–	–	–	–	–	–	x
Helisoma pseudotrivolvis	x	–	–	–	–	–	–	x
Helisoma sp.	–	x	–	–	–	–	–	–
Gyraulus altissimus	x	x	–	–	–	x	x	x
Gyraulus circumstriatus	–	–	x	–	–	x	–	–
Gyraulus deflectus obliquus	–	–	–	–	–	–	x	–
Gyraulus sp.	–	–	–	–	–	–	x	–
Vallonia gracilicosta	x	–	x	–	x	x	–	–
Succinea grosvenori	x	–	–	–	–	–	–	–
Succinea grosvenori gelida	x	–	x	cf.	x	x	–	–
Succinea ovalis pleistocenica	x	–	–	–	–	–	–	–
Gastrocopta armifera abbreviata	–	–	–	–	–	x	–	–
Gastrocopta pentodon	x	–	–	–	–	–	–	–
Gastrocopta tappaniana	x	–	–	–	–	–	–	–
Menetus dilatatus	–	–	–	–	–	–	x	–
Euconulus fulvus	x	–	–	–	x	–	–	–
Gonyodiscus anthonyi	x	–	x	–	x	x	–	–
Stagnicola palustris elodis	x	–	–	–	–	–	–	–
Valvata tricarinata	–	–	–	–	–	–	x	–
Amnicola gelida	–	–	–	–	–	–	x	–
Amnicola leightoni	–	–	–	–	–	–	x	x
Retinella hammonis	x	–	x	–	x	–	–	–
Wood fragments								
Unidentified	x	–	–	x	–	–	–	–

[1]Key to localities:

  a. Humus zone overlying calcareous till-like material in the NE ¼ SE ¼ sec. 16, T. 11 N., R. 7 W. (South Otter Twp.) (geologic section 41).

  b. Silt underlying till in the NW ¼ NW ¼ NE ¼ sec. 16, T. 11 N., R. 7 W. (South Otter Twp.) (geologic section 42).

  c. Silt underlying humus and clay in the NE ¼ SE ¼ sec. 9, T. 11 N., R. 7 W. (South Otter Twp.) (geologic section 43).

  d. Clay underlying Illinoian till and overlying peat in the SE ¼ sec. 10, T. 11 N., R. 7 W. (South Otter Twp.) (geologic section 46).

  e. Silt overlying calcareous till and underlying a humus zone under Illinoian till in the SE ¼ NE ¼ sec. 30, T. 10 N., R. 6 W. (Shaw Point Twp.) (geologic section 39).

  f. Till or till-like material underlying humus in the center NE ¼ sec. 27, T. 10 N., R. 7 W. (Carlinville Twp.) (geologic section 47).

  g. Marl, in stream bed, overlying peat in the NW ¼ NW ¼ sec. 13, T. 12 N., R. 7 W. (North Otter Twp.) (geologic section 50).

  h. Peaty silt, 5 to 7 feet below the marl.

Illinois State Geological Survey

Bulletin 77, 1952